Easy PC
interfacing

Other Computer Titles of Similar Interest

Easy PC interfacing

Robert Penfold

Bernard Babani (publishing) Ltd
The Grampians
Shepherds Bush Road
London W6 7NF
England
www.babanibooks.com

Please note

Although every care has been taken with the production of this book to ensure that any projects, designs, modifications, and/or programs, etc., contained herewith, operate in a correct and safe manner and also that any components specified are normally available in Great Britain, the Publisher and Author do not accept responsibility in any way for the failure (including fault in design) of any projects, design, modification, or program to work correctly or to cause damage to any equipment that it may be connected to or used in conjunction with, or in respect of any other damage or injury that may be caused, nor do the Publishers accept responsibility in any way for the failure to obtain specified components.

Notice is also given that if any equipment that is still under warranty is modified in any way or used or connected with home-built equipment then that warranty may be void.

First published - June 2002
Reprinted - December 2004

British Library Cataloguing in Publication Data

A catalogue record for this book is available from the British Library

ISBN   0 85934 523 8

Cover Design by Gregor Arthur

Printed and bound in Great Britain by Cox & Wyman

Preface

The "PC" has for many years been the standard computer for office use, and it also has a strong following amongst home users and in some niche markets. Specialist hardware add-ons is certainly one of these niche markets, and a PC is the standard choice for scientific, educational, and hobby users who require a computer to form the basis of all sorts of weird and wonderful gadgets. With the right add-on equipment a PC can operate as a weather station, a piece of electronic test gear, the ultimate in model train controllers, or just about anything else. Designing and building your own PC add-ons is not particularly difficult, but the stumbling block for many wannabe add-on builders is the interfacing of the gadget to the PC. How do you actually get the signals into and out of a PC and control your gadgets properly?

A PC can actually interface to your peripheral devices by way of several routes. One of these is via the standard ISA expansion slots, but this is relatively difficult and is not ideal for beginners. This method is well suited to the more advanced user who can tackle double-sided printed circuit boards. Easier options are provided in the form of the standard parallel and serial ports. In this book all three methods are covered in some detail, including tried and tested circuits for any necessary hardware. The software side of things is also covered, including both MS/DOS and Windows programming. With the Windows "visual" approach to programming it is often possible to produce sophisticated control programs for your add-ons that contain remarkably little program code. You certainly do not need to be an expert programmer in order to produce good quality software for your hardware projects.

This book is based on "How to interface PCs (BP 467), but it has been greatly expanded from the original. In fact the present book is about twice the size of its predecessor. Windows programming is an increasingly important aspect of PC interfacing, and this area has therefore been given substantially greater coverage. Much of the additional coverage concerns the use of Visual BASIC with user add-ons. There is also a new section covering the combined game and MIDI port. All the other chapters have been updated and expanded.

The risks of damaging a PC by connecting it to your own circuits are probably quite small, especially if you only use the parallel and serial ports. However, it is perhaps worth making the point that most do-it-yourself PC add-ons do not require a powerful PC, and can breathe new life into an old and otherwise unused PC. You can then experiment with PC add-ons more or less risk-free while being environmentally sound!

Robert Penfold

Trademarks

Contents

1

PC basics 1

2

ISA bus interfacing 37

3

Printer port interfacing 79

4

Serial port interfacing 141

5

Game port interfacing 171

6

Bits and PCs.............................. 199

7

Windows programming 225

PC basics

User port?

Some of the popular eight-bit computers of the 1980s came equipped
with a user port and (or) some sort of expansion port that provided an
easy means of connecting do-it-yourself add-ons. Modern 32-bit
computers are generally somewhat less accommodating. User ports
seem to be non-existent on modern computers, and a proper expansion
port is by no means a universal feature. Despite this, 32-bit machines do
have some potential for the electronic hobbyist, scientist, etc., who needs
to use a computer in measurement and control applications. The PCs
are probably more accommodating in this respect than any other current
computer, not that there are that many computers to choose from these
days.

There is no true PC equivalent to the user port of eight-bit computers
such as the BBC Model B and the Commodore 64. These user ports are
basically eight-bit parallel ports with each line individually programmable
as an input or an output. Additionally there are two handshake lines,
plus two sixteen bit timer-counters. This type of port makes it very easy
to interface a wide range of circuits to the computer.

The nearest PC equivalent to a user port is a parallel input/output card
added into one of the expansion slots. Such cards are produced
commercially, but can be very difficult to track down these days. They
can, of course, be home constructed if you are not daunted by the
prospect of tackling do-it-yourself double-sided printed circuit boards.
A standard PC parallel printer port makes quite a good alternative to a
user port, and this aspect of PC interfacing is covered in chapter 3. A
printer port lacks some of the versatility of a proper user port, and has no
counter/timer facility for example. However, it is adequate for interfacing
many user add-ons to a PC.

Fig.1.1 The AGP slot is on the right and the AMR slot is the small one towards the top left-hand corner

ISA or PCI

PCs do have something broadly comparable to the expansion ports of the old eight-bit computers. This is in the form of the vacant expansion slots within the computer. From the electrical point of view, some of these are very similar indeed to traditional expansion ports. Matters are complicated by the fact that modern PCs often have three types of expansion slot. The AGP variety is only intended for video cards and are of no use for general interfacing. In Figure 1.1 the AGP slot is the one on the right-hand side that is offset towards the front of the computer. Many PCs have small expansion slots such as the AMR type, but these are for specific types of hardware such as a modem. Again, these are not suitable for user add-ons. In Figure 1.1 there is an AMR slot near the left-hand edge of the motherboard.

The two forms of expansion slot for general interfacing are the ISA and PCI varieties. ISA expansion slots (more or less) interface direct to the

Fig.1.2 The ISA slots are the larger and darker ones on the left

buses of the microprocessor and are therefore relatively easy to use. The drawback of ISA interfacing is that this type of expansion slot is being phased out. The motherboard shown in Figure 1.1 for instance, has three types of expansion slot, but none of these are ISA slots. There are still new PCs that have one or two ISA expansion slots, and there must be millions of PCs in use around the world that have ISA slots. It will be some years yet before this type of interface is genuinely obsolete. On the other hand, over the next few years it will be necessary to move over to a different method of PC interfacing. If your PC has ISA expansion slots it is not difficult to spot them. They are larger than the other types and are usually near the left-hand edge of the board (Figure 1.2).

On the face of it, PCI slots provide the obvious alternative. In practice this interface is far from straightforward to use. A PCI slot is really a form of port and it does not give access to the microprocessor's buses. It actually has its own multiplexed data and address bus. This obviously complicates the hardware side of things, but the controlling software is also much more involved. Interfacing your gadgets to a PCI slot might be a practical proposition, but it is certainly not easy, and as such falls outside the scope of this book. There are PCI prototyping boards that have the basic interface circuitry, and using one of these might provide a relatively easy introduction to this method of PC interfacing for those who are determined to give it a try. These boards are not widely available though, and might difficult to track down.

Slot machines

From the physical point of view, ISA slots are clearly a rather different proposition to the old style expansion ports. A normal expansion port consists physically of a multi-way connector on the exterior of the computer. Only one add-on at a time can be fitted to the port unless some form of expansion system is used. Normally the add-on simply plugs straight onto the port, or it connects to it via a multi-way cable terminated in a suitable connector. This second method is the one that is generally the easier to implement, and it is the one I tend to favour for do-it-yourself add-ons.

With a PC there is no need for any expansion units to accommodate several user add-ons. Most PCs have three or more free expansion slots for this type of thing. In the, past multi-function cards helped to keep a reasonable number of slots free on computers that had to be well equipped with ports, etc. These days there is usually a fair range of ports provided on the motherboard, and in some cases the sound and video are also provided by the motherboard. This usually leaves several free expansion slots.

It is only fair to point out that some PCs, particularly some of the very small types, do not have many free slots once they have been equipped with the bare necessities for normal PC computing. In most examples there are actually several free slots, but for one reason or another they are mostly inaccessible. With PCs that have low-profile cases you may find that there are no free slots unless you are prepared to go without one of the normal necessities such as a modem. If you are interested in do-it-yourself PC interfacing there is a lot to be said for a traditional PC case and motherboard, with lots of free slots and space inside the case.

Pros and cons

Having the add-on cards inside the computer has its advantages and drawbacks. On the plus side, there is no need worry about connecting cables getting broken. Neither is there a problem with units fitted on the back of the computer getting in the way, or becoming accidentally detached. Units that mount direct onto expansion ports at the rear of computers are notorious for crashing the computer if they should be accidentally knocked. In the past there were one or two units of this type that had a reputation for crashing the computer if you should happen to breathe too hard near them! With the cards mounted securely inside the computer there is no real problem with unreliability even if the computer should take a few knocks.

The main drawback from the do-it-yourself point of view is that any add-on circuit must be on an accurate double-sided printed circuit board of irregular shape. This should be fitted with a metal mounting bracket so that the board can be firmly bolted in place. Unfortunately, the metal mounting bracket has a fairly elaborate shape that makes it a bit tricky for home construction. Connections to the outside world are via connectors mounted at the rear edge of the printed circuit board.

In order to tackle this type of thing you need to have a fair amount of experience at electronics construction, and a fair degree of expertise. There are ways of making things a little easier though. If you do not feel competent to etch and drill your own double-sided printed circuit boards, or simply do not have the necessary facilities to handle this type of thing, there are companies that can produce prototype boards if you can provide them with reasonable artwork for the board design. However, having one-off boards made can be quite expensive. Whether or not this method is practical depends on how much you are prepared to pay, and on what sort of deal you can negotiate with a printed circuit manufacturing company. For this type of thing a small company is likely to be a better bet than one which normally produces a few thousand boards at a time.

Proprietary Cards

An alternative approach is to use a proprietary printed circuit board rather than a custom type. Ordinary stripboards, etc., are not much use in this context, where a double-sided edge connector is needed to make the connections to an expansion slot. It is actually possible to make up an edge connector to fit an expansion slot, and to fit this onto a piece of stripboard. The edge connector should be fitted with pins so that you can easily make connections from the connector/slot to the stripboard. In theory you can easily make up prototype circuits on the stripboard, and wire them to the expansion slot. The system is reusable in that fresh pieces of stripboard can be fitted to the new connector when new circuits must be developed. Connections to the outside world can be made via a connector fitted on the stripboard, or by way of a flying lead (the latter probably representing the more practical solution).

While this all sounds fine in theory, and will work to some extent in practice, it is a method that I have found to be less than perfect. The main problem is that modern stripboard is not particularly tough, and in fairness it must be said that it is not intended for this type of use. This method tends to be frustrating and expensive, as the stripboard tends to break at the join with the edge connector. If you decide to adopt this method you therefore need to proceed with caution, and must treat the board/connector assembly with the proverbial "kid gloves". This method has to be regarded as considerably less than ideal for either prototyping purposes or finished cards.

What is probably a better approach is to use one of the proprietary prototyping cards which are specifically designed for PC prototyping (but which are also suitable for final units). A slight problem with these is that they do not seem to be very widely available in the U.K., and they are becoming scarcer as ISA slots become less popular. At the time of writing this, a few PC prototyping boards are available from the larger electronic component retailers. Unfortunately, those that are available tend to be quite expensive. They vary in sophistication from simple double-sided boards with no electronics, through to boards which have buffers, an address decoder, breadboards, etc. For most do-it-yourself enthusiasts only the simple boards are a practical proposition, as anything beyond this tends to be prohibitively expensive. Even simple prototyping boards tend to cost much more than stripboard, etc., of a similar size, but they are usually high quality fibreglass boards. In view of this, I suppose that they actually offer quite good value for money.

DIY Prototype Cards

Of course, it is quite possible to build for yourself something comparable to these ready made prototyping cards. However, I think that even if you were fairly expert at making double-sided printed circuit boards it would be necessary to settle for a simplified version of a proprietary board. One problem is simply that it could take weeks to manually drill the thousands of holes in one of these cards! Having the holes through plated is useful, but is probably not something for the do-it-yourself board maker to bother with.

An approach to home produced prototype boards that I have found useful is to have an edge connector which does not have any pads connecting

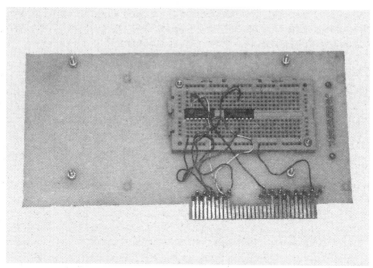

Fig.1.3 A home constructed PC prototyping system

to terminals that will, in all probability, never be needed for any of your prototype circuits. The functions of the terminals on the edge connector, plus their relative importance, is something that will be discussed more fully later in this chapter. However, it is fair to say that less than half of these terminals actually need to be used for most do-it-yourself expansion cards. Leaving out some of the "fingers" of the edge connector does not actually simplify things very much, but not having to bother with tracks and pads to connect to them can help simplify things a great deal. It also leaves more room for pads and tracks that will actually be of use.

On the main part of the board it is probably best to settle for some DIL clusters to take integrated circuits, including one or two 40-pin types to accommodate the larger integrated circuits which are a feature of so many computer add-ons. Remember that if you use 20 and 40-pin clusters, between them these will also accommodate most other sizes of integrated circuit, albeit with some pads left unused. Most devices having 0.3-inch row spacing will fit the 20-pin clusters, and most that have 0.6-inch row spacing are compatible with the 40-pin clusters. Each pad of each cluster can connect to a row of pads, and some rows of stripboard style pads can be used to provide a general prototyping area for discrete component amplifiers, oscillators, or whatever.

Even using this approach there will be a large number of holes to drill, but nothing like as many as would be needed if the entire board were covered with holes on a 0.1-inch matrix. You can actually eliminate most of the hole drilling by leaving the main part of the board blank. You can then bolt onto this area a piece of stripboard, or any form of general-purpose prototyping board. This includes solderless breadboards, which are perfectly suitable for most PC prototype circuits (but which are obviously not really appropriate to finished units). A card of this type enables new circuits to be rapidly checked and (hopefully) perfected, and can be used over and over again. Figure 1.3 shows a simple home constructed prototyping board. It is shown fitted with a solderless breadboard, but stripboard, etc., can be bolted to the board instead. It has provision for a connector at one end, which is useful if a large number of connections to the outside world are required.

Properly addressed

For the ultimate in convenience when PC prototyping you can build a card along the lines just described, but include an address decoder on the card. This avoids having to make up an address decoder each time you test a new circuit, and keeps things as quick and simple as possible. This is certainly the type of prototyping card I favour, and is the one I normally use when checking PC prototype circuits. Ideally the address decoder should have several outputs representing different address ranges, or it should be switchable between several address ranges. This enables prototype circuits to be set so that they will not conflict with any user add-ons already in the computer. Address decoding is discussed later in this book.

A variation on this theme is to add an address decoder onto a proprietary PC prototyping card. Connect pins to the pads that connect to important terminals of the edge connector so that connections can be easily made to these lines. If you do not like the idea of prototyping circuits direct onto the board, simply fit it with stripboard, a couple of breadboards, or whatever. This arrangement gives you a very versatile prototyping system, and avoids the need to make up a difficult double-sided printed circuit board. I suppose that you could even make up finished circuits on stripboard or some similar proprietary board, mount it on a ready made PC prototyping card and then wire it to the edge connector. This would not give the neatest of results, but it should work well enough in practice.

If you require the simplest means of PC interfacing, the obvious approach is to have an edge connector to fit the expansion bus, with a ribbon cable connected to this. Your add-on circuits can then be connected to the opposite end of this cable, and situated outside the PC. They can be breadboarded, constructed on stripboard, or built using any desired method. This is the PC equivalent to the method used for most do-it-yourself add-ons for eight-bit computers. Unfortunately, in my experience at any rate, this system has proved to be a bit unreliable when applied to PC add-ons. The problem is presumably due to the higher clock frequencies used for PCs, especially the "turbo" PCs that are now the norm.

It would be wrong to say that this method is totally impractical, but it can be difficult to get it to work reliably in practice. The chances of it working with a long connecting cable are small, and the shorter the cable, the better the chances of success. The slower the bus speed the greater the chances of reliable operation. In the past PCs often had a "jumper" on the motherboard that could be used to select a slow or a fast expansion bus clock frequency. Some PCs had a setting or settings in the ROM BIOS Setup program that provided some degree of control over the expansion bus timing. With some computers the expansion bus speed is dependent on the main system clock frequency. Switching from the "turbo" mode to the normal one would then slow down the expansion bus. Facilities such as these as these do not seem to be included in modern PCs, which generally operate the ISA bus at 8MHz. Consequently, unless you are using a true "golden oldie" PC there will be no control over the speed of the ISA bus.

Expansion bus history

Many aspects of PC computing have developed substantially over the years, and the expansion bus is no exception. The original PC/XT bus is an eight-bit type. This may seem strange, since the PCs are 32-bit computers. However, bear in mind that the original PCs were 16-bit computers. Furthermore, the 8088 microprocessor used in the original PCs (and many early "clones") is a so-called "cut down" version of the 8086 microprocessor. This basically just means that it has an eight-bit data bus and must take in data and output it eight bits at a time. Operations on 16-bit chunks of data in memory must therefore be accomplished using what are effectively two eight-bit instructions rather than a single 16-bit type.

Once data is inside the microprocessor's internal registers it is handled as 16-bit chunks, and internally the 8088 is a true 16-bit microprocessor. The eight-bit data bus gives some speed disadvantage compared to the

8086, but the speed difference in practical applications is not very large. Although the 8088 has an eight-bit bus, because it is a proper 16-bit component in other respects, the PCs that are based on this chip are usually regarded as 16-bit machines rather than superior eight-bit types, but I suppose this is a matter of opinion.

It is perhaps worth mentioning that some XT class PCs did actually have an 8086 microprocessor. Despite this, they usually retained the standard eight-bit expansion bus in order to give full compatibility with 8088 based XT type PCs. Not many PCs based on the 8086 were ever produced, and certain Olivetti and Amstrad PCs are probably the only examples of popular PCs of this type. Of course, these PCs are now well and truly obsolete.

AT PCs

The first development of the PC expansion bus was the 16-bit type. This became necessary when AT (advanced technology) PCs came along. These have an 80286 microprocessor, which is a full 16-bit type, complete with a 16-bit data bus. Presumably it would have been possible to have an ordinary eight-bit expansion bus on these computers, but it would have removed some of the potential advantages of using the 80286. The solution was to retain the standard eight-bit bus, but to augment it with some further lines carried on a second edge connector mounted in front of the existing connector. This enables appropriate eight-bit cards to be used with an AT computer, but still enables 16-bit cards to be used where these offer advantages. This 16-bit PC expansion bus is often called the "ISA" bus, and "ISA" simply stands for "Industry Standard Architecture". In modern PCs the two connectors are merged into a single moulding, but you can still clearly see the separate sets of terminals.

Old buses

Note that PC compatibles that are based on the 80386SX 16-bit microprocessor are basically just AT computers, and are interfaced in the same way. Similarly, PCs that are based on the 80386, 80486SX, and 80486 32-bit microprocessors are essentially AT type PCs. They do sometimes have a 32-bit expansion bus, but in most cases only one slot is of this type. It is normally in the form of a standard 16-bit PC expansion bus with an extra edge connector mounted in front. This added edge connector carries the extra lines needed for 32-bit interfacing. There is no true standard for these 32-bit slots though, and they normally only accept memory expansion cards produced specially for each make of computer. These 32-bit expansion buses are now long obsolete anyway, and are something that will not be considered further here.

There is actually a standard 32-bit PC expansion bus, which is the result of agreements between several major manufacturers of PC compatibles. This is the "EISA" ("Extended Industry Standard Architecture") bus. From the physical point of view this is substantially different to the 32-bit expansion buses of ISA 80386 and 80486 PCs. It has the normal ISA bus, but an extra connector alongside this provides the additional lines needed for 32-bit interfacing. It is a high-speed bus that has definite advantages over the standard ISA bus for advanced applications that genuinely require very high-speed data transfers. However, for many purposes, including most user add-on applications, the ordinary ISA bus will suffice. Anyway, the EISA bus was usurped by the PCI type and it is not something we will pursue further here.

There is a fourth type of PC expansion bus, and this is IBM's MCA (Micro Channel Architecture) bus. This is another high-speed 32-bit type, and it was used on some of IBM's PCs. These computers were not really traditional PCs, and were intended to be a sort of new generation of PCs. While they had good software compatibility with ordinary PCs, they were largely incompatible as far as hardware is concerned. Consequently, interfacing to this type of PC really falls outside the scope of this book. Anyway, the MCA bus is another one that has "fallen by the wayside".

Finally, modern PCs are equipped with several PCI slots that replace some or all of the ISA expansion slots. The PCI slots offer definite advantages over the ISA type, such as higher operating speed, 32/64-bit operation, and full "plug and play" support. As pointed out previously, in the fullness of time PCI slots will totally replace the ISA variety, and a fair percentage of new PCs do not have any ISA slots. Also as explained previously, interfacing via the PCI bus seems to be extremely complex, and it would not appear to support any form of basic interfacing suitable for DIY add-ons. Using the PCI bus is certainly well beyond the scope of the present publication.

Although modern PCs are based on Pentium or equivalent processors, they are still essentially AT "clones", and provided they have the standard ports they can be interfaced to the outside world in much the same way as the original PCs. Most of the information in this book therefore applies equally to an old PC XT clone, a modern PC using an Intel or AMD processor, or anything in between.

The ISA Bus

The ISA bus has a two by 31-way 0.1-inch pitch edge connector to carry the basic eight-bit section of the bus. The female connectors are on the computer's motherboard, while the add-on cards must have a male edge connector. This male edge connector is basically just a protrusion on the card, which has the 31 "fingers" of copper on both sides of the board. The extra lines for 16-bit interfacing are carried by a two by 18-way edge connector mounted in front of the two by 31-way connector. Figure 1.4 gives details of this arrangement, including the standard method of pin numbering used for both connectors.

This is a list of the lines available on the eight-bit expansion bus:

Terminal No.	Function
A1	-I/O CH CK
A2	D7
A3	D6
A4	D5
A5	D4
A6	D3
A7	D2
A8	D1
A9	D0
A10	I/O CH RDY
A11	AEN
A12	A19
A13	A18
A14	A17
A15	A16
A16	A15
A17	A14
A18	A13
A19	A12

A20	A11
A21	A10
A22	A9
A23	A8
A24	A7
A25	A6
A26	A5
A27	A4
A28	A3
A29	A2
A30	A1
A31	A0
B1	GND
B2	RESET
B3	+5V
B4	IRQ2
B5	−5V
B6	DRQ2
B7	−12V
B8	Reserved
B9	+12V
B10	GND
B11	-MEMW
B12	-MEMR
B13	-IOW
B14	-IOR
B15	-DACK3
B16	DRQ3
B17	-DACK1

B18	DRQ1
B19	-DACK0
B20	CLK
B21	IRQ7
B22	IRQ6
B23	IRQ5
B24	IRQ4
B25	IRQ3
B26	-DACK2
B27	TC
B28	ALE
B29	+5V
B30	OSC
B31	GND

(A minus sign at the beginning of a function description indicates that the line is negative active).

Many of these lines will be familiar to anyone who has undertaken interfacing on eight-bit computers, and should be particularly familiar to anyone who has dealt with computers based on the 8080 or Z80 microprocessors. However, for the benefit of those who have limited experience of computer interfacing a description of each line (or set of lines) is provided in the following sections.

Data/Address Bus

Lines D0 to D7 are the standard eight-bit bidirectional data bus. Any data provided by your add-on circuits is fed into the microprocessor via these eight lines. Similarly, any data fed from the microprocessor to your add-on circuits will come by way of these eight lines. A0 to A19 are the address bus, and are outputs provided by the microprocessor. These provide a one-megabyte address range for memory circuits. 16 and 32-bit PCs have additional address lines on the second edge connector which enables a much larger amount of memory to be accommodated.

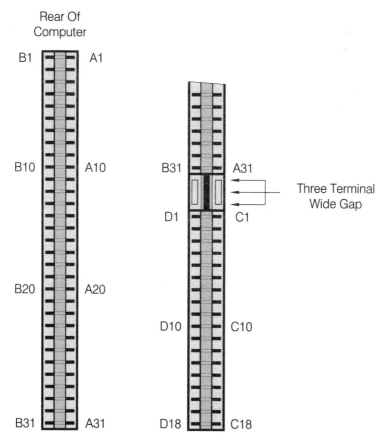

Fig.1.4 Edge connector pin numbering for 8 and 16-bit PC buses

However, PCs which have 16 or 32-bit microprocessors normally operate in an 8088 emulation mode where only the basic 20-bit address bus is utilised. These days increasing use of the extended memory of 16 and 32-bit machines is made via disc caches, DOS extenders, etc. This is largely of academic importance to the do-it-yourself add-on enthusiast, and you will normally only need address lines A0 to A19. In fact you will not normally deal with interfacing memory circuits, and will not even require all these address lines.

The address bus is also used for selecting the correct input/output circuit. In this context only the lower 16 lines (A0 to A15) are utilised. This gives some 64k of input/output address space, or some 65536 input/output addresses in other words. This is more than would ever be needed in a real computer system, and a somewhat simplified approach has therefore been used on the PCs. Only the lower ten address lines (A0 to A9) are utilised, which still gives some 1024 usable input/output addresses. The lower half of the address range is reserved for internal use (i.e. circuits on the motherboard), leaving the upper 512 addresses free for expansion cards. Many of these addresses are reserved for specific functions, such as the standard ports and disc controllers. There is still plenty of space left for your own expansion cards. The input/output map is a topic we will discuss fully later on.

Control Bus

The 8088 microprocessor has a control bus that consists of seven lines. Four of these are MEMR, MEMW, IOR, and IOW, which are all forms of read/write line. Unlike some microprocessors, the 8088 has separate read and write lines, not one line that indicates one type of operation when set high, and the opposite type when set low. Also, the 8088 has separate memory and input/output maps. 8088 based computers do not have input/output devices placed at empty spaces in the memory map, as do computers based on chips such as the 6502 and 68000. Thus, what is a single control line on some microprocessors becomes some four lines on the 8088 series. These lines are all active low. MEMR goes low when the microprocessor is reading from memory - MEMW goes low when it is writing to memory. IOR is activated when data is read from an input device - IOW is activated when data is written to an output circuit. These are obviously important lines that will often have to be decoded by your add-on circuits. Presumably any do-it-yourself add-on cards will not fit in the memory map, but will go into the input/output map. Accordingly, you will not normally need to bother with MEMR and MEMW, but will need to use IOR and IOW extensively.

ALE (address latch enable) is a control line that can be used to synchronise events to microprocessor bus cycles. This is not a line that you will normally need to bother with. The same is not true of AEN (address enable) which goes low during processor bus cycles (i.e. normal operations). It is needed to distinguish between normal bus cycles and DMA (direct memory access) cycles. This must be decoded to the low state by the address/control bus decoder.

The reset line is an output generated by the computer, which is a standard active high reset line. This goes high at switch on, or if there is a hardware reset (i.e. if you press the computer's reset button). Software resets, which includes those produced using the keyboard Control - Alt - Delete sequence, do not normally result in a reset signal being produced on the reset line. It is not essential to use this line to provide the reset signal for your add-on circuits. Some may simply not require a reset signal at all, while with others it might be easier to include a reset pulse generator circuit on the expansion card. In most cases though, where a reset signal is needed it is probably easier to use the computer's reset line. If a negative active reset signal is needed, simply feeding the reset line of the expansion port through an inverter should provide a suitable signal.

DMA/Interrupts

There are nine DMA lines. DACK0 to DACK3 are outputs, as is the TC (terminal count) line. DIRQ1 to DIRQ4 are inputs. These are lines that are only needed for circuits that make use of the advanced DMA facilities. This is not likely to include home constructed expansion cards, and we will consequently not consider the DMA lines further here.

The 8088 has eight normal interrupt lines of the active high variety, but IRQ0 and IRQ1 are not available on the expansion bus. Neither are the special (high priority) interrupt lines such as NMI (non-maskable interrupt). Interrupt lines IRQ2 to IRQ7 are available, but bear in mind that standard expansion cards such as the serial and parallel ports will use some of these. For most user add-ons there is no need to utilise the interrupt lines, but they can be useful where it is important that the computer responds to the add-on very rapidly. Applications of this type are usually where data must be read intermittently, but when the data does come along, it does so in large quantities and at a high rate. It is important that each byte of data is read very soon after it has been received, or it may be over-written by the next byte of data. Using the interrupt lines on any computer is a fairly complex business though, and it is much easier to crash the computer than to get it right. Using interrupts on the PCs is perhaps a little less fraught than using interrupts on some of the popular eight-bit computers. Even so, this is something that is strictly for the advanced user.

Power and Clocks

The expansion bus includes two clock lines. OSC is a buffered crystal controlled oscillator signal at 14.318MHz. It is mainly included to act as the clock signal for the colour graphics adapter, and it is probably not of much use for anything else. The other clock signal is CLK, which is the system clock, which has a two to one duty cycle. For the original PCs the system clock was at 4.77MHz, but on most PC XT "clones" it is normally 8MHz, 10MHz, or even higher. On AT class computers the clock frequency can be practically anything from 6MHz to 450MHz. AT type PCs used to have the ability to operate at a "normal" clock frequency of about 8MHz, and a "turbo" mode of around 20MHz to 50MHz (4.77MHz and about 8MHz to 15MHz for XT class PCs). With Pentium PCs the "turbo" switch is normally absent (or present but it does not actually do anything), and the computer always operates at its maximum clock frequency.

Clearly the system clock signal can not be relied upon to be at a certain frequency. On AT computers it may well be missing, with no connection made to this terminal of the expansion bus. These factors must be borne in mind when designing an interface that uses this clock signal. Of course, if you are only producing a card for your own use in a computer where this clock signal is present, and will always be at a certain frequency, then you can design the card on the basis of a known and reliable clock frequency. Remember though, that if you change to a different PC you may have to modify the card in order to get it to function correctly with the new computer. In general it is better to simply ignore both the clock signals on the expansion bus, and where necessary include a suitable clock generator on the expansion card.

Four power supplies plus the 0 volt earth (ground) rail are available on the expansion bus. The available voltages are +5V, –5V, +12V, and –12V. The +5 volt rail should be able to supply several amps without any problems with overloading. It is difficult to be precise about how much power is available on this line as it depends on the rating of the power supply unit, and the current drawn by the motherboard, expansion cards, etc. Some PCs have massive power supplies and hardware that has very modest power requirements. With these there is likely to be well over ten amps of spare current available.

At the other end of the spectrum there are mini-PCs which have relatively low-power supply units, and which might have as little as an amp or two to spare for your add-ons. Also, some PCs have hefty 300 watt power supply units, but have little spare capacity due to the high powers required by modern processors, hard disc drives, CD-RW drives, etc. Since your cards are not likely to consume a total of even one amp of current, any PC should be able to power your add-ons without any difficulty. However, it is probably best to use the PC's supply unit only for electronics. If you are using the PC to control electric motors, filament bulbs, etc., then these should have a separate power supply unit.

The +12 volt supply should also be able to provide an amp or two without any problems. In fact it might be possible to draw as much as 4 amps from the +12 volt line, but it is probably best to stick to a maximum of about 2 amps unless you can definitely ascertain that your computer can reliably supply more than this. On many PCs the +12 volt supply does not seem to be well stabilised, and often seems to be at around +13 volts. I think that I am right in stating that this supply is mainly intended for powering the motors in the disc drives, and that the latter include their own regulator circuits. It is probably not safe to assume that this line is well stabilised, or particularly noise-free. In fact you should assume that it is unstable and polluted with a lot of electrical noise.

The ratings of the negative supplies are relatively small. The –5 volt and –12 volt lines are usually rated at 0.3 amps and 0.25 amps respectively (some of which may well be consumed by other cards). It is probably best to keep the current drains from the negative supplies down to about 100 milliamps (0.1 amps) or less. In most applications the negative supplies will not be needed at all, and where they are required it will often only be necessary to draw currents of a few milliamps or less. For example, the "tail" resistor of some analogue to digital converters requires a negative supply current of well under 1 milliamp, and for a circuit that has three or four operational amplifiers a negative supply current of less that 10 milliamps would normally be needed.

The Rest

The IO CH RDY (Input/Output Channel Ready) line is an important one. It is an input that can be used to insert wait states. A wait state is simply a system clock cycle during a read or write operation where nothing happens. The purpose of introducing these "dummy" clock cycles is to slow down the computer to the point where a slow memory or input/output circuit can keep up. This might be necessary for some user add-ons. However, if at all possible it is obviously better to keep things simple by having add-on circuits that can keep up with the computer. In most cases there is no difficulty in doing this, and IO CH RDY can be ignored.

IO CHCK (Input/Output Channel Check) is an active low input line. It is taken low in order to indicate that a memory or input/output parity error has occurred. A non-maskable interrupt is then generated. This line is not normally used with user add-ons.

Sixteen-Bit Bus

Most do-it-yourself PC interfacing only requires the eight-bit bus, but I suppose that there are some applications that would benefit from use of the full 16-bit bus. This is a list of the extra functions available on the 16-bit ISA bus.

Terminal No.	Function
D1	-MEM CS16
D2	-I/O CS16
D3	IRQ16
D4	IRQ11
D5	IRQ12
D6	IRQ15
D7	IRQ14
D8	-DACK0
D9	DRQ0
D10	-DAQ10
D11	DRQ5
D12	-DACK6
D13	DRQ6
D14	-DACK7
D15	DRQ7
D16	+5V
D17	-MASTER
D18	GND
C1	BHE
C2	A23
C3	A22
C4	A21
C5	A20

C6	A19
C7	A18
C8	A17
C9	-MEMR
C10	-MEMW
C11	D8
C12	D9
C13	D10
C14	D11
C15	D12
C16	D13
C17	D14
C18	D15

(A minus sign at the beginning of a function description indicates that the line is negative active).

When a PC is equipped with a 16-bit bus there are actually a few changes to the basic eight-bit bus. -DACK0 for instance, becomes -REFRESH on the 16-bit bus. -REFRESH simple indicates that a memory refresh cycle is in progress. This is really only of academic importance since it is highly unlikely that you would ever use one of the lines which is subject to these variations of usage. Most of the extra lines on the 16-bit bus are of no interest to the do-it-yourself interfacing enthusiast. The extra address lines are only needed when accessing extended memory, and are irrelevant to input/output devices. Most of the other lines are interrupt and DMA lines, etc., which you will probably not need to use either.

Of course, the extra data lines (D8 to D15) will be needed for 16-bit interfacing, and permit data to be exchanged in 16-bit words rather than being limited to eight-bit bytes. BHE is the Bus High Enable output, and it is alternatively known as SBHE (System Bus High Enable). It indicates that data transfer is to be on the high byte (D8 to D15), as well as on the low byte (D0 to D7). Data transfers always involve the lower byte, and so there is no equivalent to this on the eight-bit bus. -MEM CS16 and -I/O CS16 are inputs that are used to inform the computer that memory and input/output data exchanges are to be 16-bit types. If suitable signals are not applied to these inputs, 16-bit data transfers will be carried out as two eight-bit transfers.

Important Lines

Clearly a large number of the lines included on the expansion bus will not be needed for most interfacing. The terminals of the edge connector that connect to unused lines can obviously be omitted. This can help to simplify the printed circuit boards if you are using custom printed circuit boards. It can massively simplify things if you are making up your own prototyping boards. This is a list of the terminals of the edge connector that you will often need to implement, and which should certainly be include in PC prototyping systems.

Terminal	Function
A2	D7
A3	D6
A4	D5
A5	D4
A6	D3
A7	D2
A8	D1
A9	D0
A11	AEN
A22	A9
A23	A8
A24	A7
A25	A6
A26	A5
A27	A4
A28	A3
A29	A2
A30	A1

A31	A0
B1	0V (GND)
B2	RESET
B3	+5V
B5	−5V
B7	−12V
B9	+12V
B13	-IOW
B14	-IOR

This list is basically just the lower ten lines of the address bus, the data bus, the supply lines, RESET, -IOW and -IOR. For 16-bit interfacing you will normally need these lines as well.

Terminal	**Function**
D2	-I/O CS16
C1	BHE
C11	D8
C12	D9
C13	D10
C14	D11
C15	D12
C16	D13
C17	D14
C18	D15

Getting Physical

An important aspect of PC interfacing is to get the physical dimensions of the cards spot-on. This is every bit as important as getting things right electronically. Make small errors in certain dimensions and you could find that the card would simply not fit into the computer. Make the edge connector inaccurately and the may well short circuit adjacent pairs of contacts from one end of the expansion slot to the other! This might not actually do any damage to the computer, since most logic circuits are pretty tough, and PC power supplies have comprehensive protection circuits, which should avoid catastrophe in the event of short circuits. However, with this type of thing it is best not to find out the hard way. If your PC should prove to be unable to withstand this type of problem, the result could be an extremely expensive repair bill. When undertaking any computer interfacing it is important to proceed very carefully indeed, taking as few risks as possible. The more expensive the computer, the more carefully you need to proceed.

I prefer not to try out prototype cards on my main PCs at all, but instead use a PC that is largely comprised of left-overs from upgrades to my main PCs, plus parts obtained cheaply at computer fairs or in swaps with friends. This PC is good enough for most PC interfacing applications, and if should come to a "sticky" end it would be unfortunate, but not a substantial loss. A major repair such as fitting a new motherboard would be an unwelcome expense, but it would not "break the bank". I could not say the same of a repair to something like a 2200MHz Pentium 4 based PC with the latest in future-proofed motherboards.

Interfacing to PCs is certainly something I would not recommend for beginners at electronics. For beginners the best advice is to gain some experience building up a few simple electronic projects before trying your hand at any form of computer interfacing. Then start with some projects that interface to a serial or parallel port. Either that or you should be prepared to write-off your PC against experience!

Dimensions

Physical details of eight and 16-bit cards are shown in Figures 1.5 and 1.6 respectively. These are largely self explanatory, but there are a few important points to note. Firstly, the length dimension given for the cards is for full-length cards. Obviously cards do not have to be full-length types, and probably most PC expansion cards are only about half-length or less. There is no minimum acceptable size for PC cards, but there is a practical limitation in that the card must be long enough to include the full edge connector, or both connectors in the case of a 16-bit card.

Of course, if a card is less than full length, it is the front part of the card that is cut down to size. The edge connector and mounting bracket at the rear of the card make it unacceptable to shorten this end. It is probably

Fixing
Bracket

2.54mm

23mm

81mm

338mm

8 Bit Expansion Card (Full Length)

107mm Max.

Fig. 1.5 Physical details for a full length eight-bit expansion card

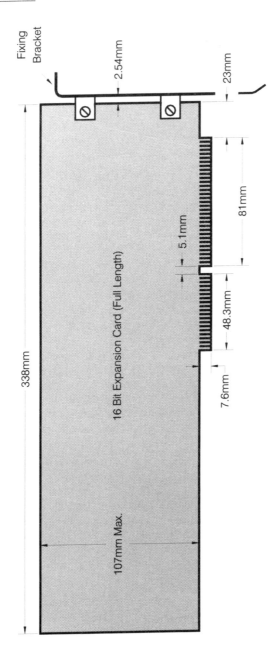

Fig.1.6 A 16-bit expansion card is basically just an 8-bit type having an extra edge connector

not a good idea to produce cards that are just fractionally less than full length. It would seem to be better to make such cards full length, so that the guide rails in the computer properly support the front end of the card. Unfortunately, these guide-rails are not included in some modern PCs, but it makes sense to use them when they are available.

PC expansion cards are generally about 100 millimetres (4 inches) high, excluding the edge connector. With most computers it is safe to have cards of up to about 4.2 inches in height, but above this you may find the card will fit all right, but that the lid of the case can not be closed properly. With some mini PC cases it is necessary to have cards no more than about 4 inches high. There is no minimum height for PC cards, but there are again practical limitations. If you make cards much less than 100 millimetres high it may be very difficult to slot them in place and to remove them again, as there is very little to get hold of. I generally make PC expansion cards 100 millimetres high and a minimum of about 125 millimetres long, even if this gives an area that is far larger than the interface circuit really requires.

Mounting bracket

Making your own fixing brackets is a bit tricky as they have a quite intricate shape. I will not give any details of fixing brackets here, as the best route to making your own is to copy a blanking plate from one of the expansion slots in your PC. You might actually have one or two spare blanking plates, where these plates have been removed to make way for added expansion cards. Unfortunately, modern cases often have blanking plates that are simply broken away from the case when they are not required, rather than the type that is released via a fixing screw. These are likely to be of little help.

Where it is possible to obtain "proper" blanking plates it will almost certainly be easier to use these for your home constructed cards than to try making your own brackets. Of course, a fixing bracket is not absolutely essential, and PC cards fit quite firmly into the expansion slots. If the bracket is omitted it is unlikely that the card will be pulled out of place provided you take reasonable care. It is clearly preferable to include mounting brackets, but many constructors of PC expansion cards prefer to simply omit them altogether. I must admit that I avoid using them whenever possible.

Although in Figures 1.5 and 1.6 the mounting brackets are shown as being fitted to the boards via simple right-angled brackets, these brackets are often unnecessary. Often PC cards are fitted with right angled D connectors to permit connections to be made to the outside world. In such cases the D connectors will normally provide a convenient means of fixing the mounting bracket to the board. A suitable cutout for the connector must be made in the bracket, and this can be cut using a miniature file or a coping saw.

If you are lucky, you may already have one or two brackets which have cutouts for one or two D connectors. Multi-function cards are often supplied with brackets of this type. These cards often require more sockets than it is possible to accommodate on the rear section of the card. The extra sockets must therefore be mounted on blanking plates for unused expansion slots, and connected to the card via jumper leads. Many PC cases have mounting holes for D connectors in the rear panel of the case. You can then use these instead of the drilled blanking plates, leaving the latter free for use with your own expansion cards.

Various odds and ends of use to the home constructor are available from most computer fairs. It is usually possible to obtain brackets fitted with connectors, and cheap expansion cards that are fitted with mounting brackets. In either case it is not usually too difficult to remove the bracket and adapt it for use with your own cards. Clearly it is not worthwhile spending a lot of money on an expansion card in order to get a metal bracket, but this is a good way of doing things if you can buy an obsolete card at a "bargain basement" price.

If you make your own mounting brackets, unless you have access to some advanced metal working facilities it will be much easier to use thin (about 18 s.w.g.) aluminium than heavy gauge steel. Whatever means you adopt for mounting the bracket on the expansion card make sure that it is the correct distance from the rear of the card. Small errors here can make it impossible to fit the card into the computer.

Programming

The hardware of a PC is normally handled via DOS routines or Windows drivers, but your home constructed expansion cards will usually be types that have no DOS or Windows support. Your only means of reading from them or writing data to them is to directly access the hardware via a suitable programming language. Some languages are better for this type of thing than are others. It is only fair to point out that some PC languages in their raw state are of no use whatever in this context. They simply do not provide instructions that give direct access to devices in the input/output map. There are add-ons that can provide the missing instructions for some languages, so this problem is not necessarily insurmountable.

It also has to be pointed out that some operating systems prevent direct accessing of ports. In particular, it is not allowed under Windows NT4, 2000, and XP. Again, it might be possible to access your circuits using an add-on to the programming language, so that it can be controlled via the operating system. However, this may not be possible in all cases, and it will certainly complicate matters where it is an option. Windows 98 or ME are better choices for a computer that will be used with your own circuits.

Some add-on enthusiasts avoid Windows altogether, and simply boot the computer into MS-DOS using a floppy disc containing GW BASIC. A 1.44-megabyte floppy disc is sufficient to take the system files, GW BASIC, and a number of programs. The drawback of this method is that it is much more difficult to produce programs that have a modern interface. Even for very simple projects, Windows programming languages have huge advantages. For example, using a Windows programming language there is no difficulty in producing readouts having large digits. You simply set a suitably large font size. This type of thing is much more difficult using GW BASIC or QBASIC where the machine font is normally used to print things on the screen.

Assembler

Obviously there should be no problem when using assembly language or machine code since you have direct access to the instructions of the microprocessor, including the ones that give access the input and output circuits. Some high-level computer languages enable programs to call and run assembly language routines, and this provides a means of controlling user add-ons. Note that with both types of assembler the Windows NT4, 2000, and XP restrictions on directly accessing the hardware still apply.

A combination of BASIC and assembler is a method that was much used with eight-bit computers running interpreted BASICs. These languages almost invariably provided instructions that could be used to control user add-ons, but for some applications they would simply run too slowly. A mixture of BASIC and assembly language gives the convenience of the former, with the speed of the latter when required. This is a system that I have always found to be very good in practice, but the speed of compiled languages for 16/32-bit computers tends to make it less attractive in a

PC context. However, it is an approach that could be well suited to some situations, and it is certainly something worth keeping in mind.

GW and QBASIC

The BASIC supplied with most PC compatibles in the past was Microsoft's GW BASIC, which is an interpreted BASIC. This was later replaced with a modernised but largely compatible programming language called QBASIC, which is also an interpreted language. This makes GW BASIC and QBASIC easy to use, but they are not fast by PC language standards. These languages have benefited from the speed of modern PCs though. The speed of current PCs is such that you can often do things with an interpreted language that would have required a compiled language with early PCs.

On modern PCs GW BASIC and QBASIC are good enough for many applications, but it is definitely a case of "doing things the hard way" unless you require the most simple of user interfaces. On the other hand, they are languages I would certainly recommend when initially experimenting with PC add-ons. Using the direct modes you can write data to and read it from ports without running a program. This is ideal for experimenting and learning about computer interfacing.

In GW BASIC or QBASIC the OUT instruction is used to write data to devices in the input/output map (e.g. OUT 768,12 would write a value of 12 to output address 768). Data can be read from devices in the input/ output map using the INP function. For instance, the instruction X = INP(768) would set variable X at the value read from input address 768.

I sometimes get enquiries from users of Windows 95/98 who wish to know where they can obtain either QBASIC or GW BASIC. This is not loaded as part of the "typical" installation option, but it is present on the Windows 95 and 98 CD-ROMs. In the Windows 98 upgrade CD for example, it is in the tools\oldmsdos subdirectory. It is in the same location on the Windows ME upgrade disc. Note that both QBASIC and GW BASIC are MS/DOS programs. In order to run them under Windows 95 or 98 the computer must be rebooted in MS/DOS mode, or an MS/DOS window must be used.

Most other BASICs, whether interpreted or compiled, should work perfectly well with user add-ons. The only exceptions are some of the higher level BASICs, which have mouse support, windowing facilities, etc. These often lack facilities for direct accessing of the hardware. Microsoft's Visual BASIC is good example of a PC BASIC in this category.

However, it is possible to obtain various add-ons that permit control of input/output ports. Visual BASIC is well suited to use with user add-ons, so it is worthwhile augmenting it so that it can access ports.

The abilities of other PC languages to control the computer's hardware seem to vary considerably. Most languages can actually manage this type of thing, but not necessarily in a particularly straightforward manner. If you are not an expert programmer it is probably best to use a good BASIC language. BASIC is a much-maligned programming language, but any fairly recent version should offer excellent facilities and reasonably fast operating speed. While BASIC is not well suited to all applications, it is very good indeed for measurement and control applications. It is therefore well suited to most applications that involve user add-ons.

Delphi

Borland's Delphi programming language is also worthy of consideration. This is based on their popular Turbo PASCAL language, but it is a "visual" programming language, which makes it very easy to produce sophisticated user interfaces. Using GWBASIC, QBASIC, Visual BASIC, and Delphi is covered in the final chapters of this book.

Properly Addressed

As explained previously, the input/output map for PCs consists of only 1024 addresses, because only the bottom ten address lines are used for input/output mapping. The lower half of the map is reserved for system hardware (i.e. circuits on the motherboard), while the upper half is reserved for the expansion bus. Standard circuits such as serial and parallel ports do not count as system hardware, since they fit onto the expansion bus (or they did in the original PCs anyway). This means that the 512-address range for the expansion bus is fairly crowded, with few gaps. This is the PC input/output map.

System

Hex Address Range	Function
000-01F	DMA Controller #1
020-03F	Interrupt Controller #1
040-05F	8254 Timer

060-06F	Keyboard Interface
070-07F	Real Time Clock
080-09F	DMA Page Register
0A0-0BF	Interrupt Controller #2
0C0-0DF	DMA Controller #2
0F0	Clear Processor Busy
0F1	Reset Processor
0F8 - 0FF	Arithmetic Processor

Expansion Bus

Hex Address Range	Function
1F0-1F8	Fixed Disc
200-207	Games Port
210-217	Expansion Unit
220-24F	Reserved
278-27F	Parallel Port 2
2F0-2F7	Reserved
2F8-2FF	Serial Port 2
300-31F	Prototype Card
320-32F	Fixed Disc
360-36F	Reserved
378-37F	Parallel Port 1
380-38F	SDLC Bisynchronous #2
3A0-3AF	SDLC Bisynchronous #1
3B0-3BF	Monochrome Display/Printer Adapter
3C0-3CF	Reserved
3D0-3DF	Colour Graphics Adapter
3F0-3F7	Floppy Disc Controller
3F8-3FF	Serial Port 1

It might actually be possible to exploit some of the lower 512 addresses for user add-ons, but this would not be doing things in standard PC fashion, and is best avoided. It could easily lead to problems. Although the upper half of the address range is pretty crowded, there are some areas here, which can be exploited for user add-ons. In particular, there are 32 addresses from &H300 to &H31F. These are reserved for prototype cards, and your own expansion cards could reasonably be deemed to be in this category. It is an area of the memory map that you should be able to use without any real risk of clashes with existing hardware.

However, some soundcards and integrated audio systems use these addresses for the MIDI interface. Where possible, the MIDI interface should be disabled or moved to another address range. With an integrated audio system it is usually possible to switch off the MIDI interface via the computer's BIOS Setup program. One or two alternative address ranges might also be available. With a modern PC the MIDI interface might be disabled by default, but it is as well to check this point before trying to use this address range. With a soundcard you should consult the instruction manual to see if it is possible to disable the MIDI port or alter its address range.

Address checking

With a PC running Windows 95, 98, or ME it is easy to determine which memory addresses are in use. The System Information utility can be used to show an input/output map for the computer. This program can be launched by going to the Start menu and then choosing Programs, Accessories, System Tools, and System Information. This produces an initial window that gives some basic information about the PC and the Windows installation. In the left-hand section of the window, double-click the Hardware Resources entry to expand it, and then double-click the I/O entry. After a short delay the right-hand section of the window will show an I/O map for the computer.

With my main PC the MIDI port is reported as being present at hexadecimal addresses 0300 and 0301. However, the BIOS Setup program gave the option of disabling the port or moving it to another address range, so there was an easy way around this problem. If the port genuinely only uses the two lowest addresses in this block there should be no problem in leaving the MIDI port active and using the other 30 addresses. Problems would only occur if the MIDI port's address decoder circuit used less than full decoding, giving "echoes" of the hardware at other addresses in the &H300 to &H31F range. Any gap in the upper half of the address range should be usable.

If the &H300 to &H31F range is available, 32 addresses is not a great deal when compared to the number available on some other computers, such as the old BBC Model B computers with their two pages (512 addresses) of available address space on the expansion bus. However, this should be perfectly adequate for most users. It is sufficient for several parallel port cards, plus some analogue converter boards, or whatever.

If 32 addresses are deemed inadequate there are ways around the problem. As already pointed out, any addresses in the upper half of the memory map, which are not actually occupied by hardware in your computer, can safely be used. This statement has to be qualified somewhat, as the real situation is that addresses of this type can be used safely by you with your particular PC system. It can not be assumed that home constructed cards that use these addresses can also be used successfully with other PCs.

In practice, provided you use addresses that are reserved for an unusual piece of hardware, it is unlikely that there will be any problems. Something like the address space for the second serial or parallel port would not be a wise choice, but using the address space reserved for the SDLC Bisynchronous Port #2 would seem to be a very safe bet. There are actually a few small gaps in the input/output map which do not seem to be allocated to anything, and it would presumably be perfectly alright to exploit one or more of these.

Another means of obtaining more addresses for your add-ons is to use some of the upper address lines that are normally left unused. For instance, you could have some add-ons that use the address space from &H300 to &H31F, but which will only be activated if address line A10 is low. You could have a second piece of hardware using the same address space, but designed to operate only when A10 is high. The first set of hardware would be accessed at addresses from &H300 to &H31F, but the second set of hardware would be at addresses from &H700 to &H71F. I have never found it necessary to adopt this method, but in theory it would enable the basic range of 32 addresses to be used many times over, giving more expansion potential than could ever be used in practice.

Finally

This covers the basics of PC interfacing in general terms. Probably the main problem for the do-it-yourself PC add-on enthusiast is that PC interfacing is a bit awkward from the mechanical point of view. However, if you use proprietary PC prototyping cards or take care to get things accurate when making your own cards, the mechanical aspects of construction should not prove to be insurmountable. In chapter 2 we will consider electronic circuits for PC address decoding, etc., and this aspect of PC interfacing is normally very straightforward. In fact interfacing to PCs is more straightforward than interfacing to many popular eight-bit computers as far as the electronics is concerned. Thankfully, the PC is free from the quirky methods of interfacing used on many eight-bit computers.

Points to remember

A PC has no user port of the type fitted to the popular eight-bit computers of yesteryear. It does not have an expansion port as such either. A PC that has ISA slots has something comparable to an expansion port, and using an ISA slot for your own add-ons is relatively straightforward. Unfortunately, the PCI bus is not in the "easy" category, and neither is USB interfacing.

Only the lowest 1024 input/output addresses are used by PCs. The lower 512 addresses are used for system hardware, and your add-ons should therefore go into the higher 512 addresses. There is no section of a PC's input/output map reserved specifically for user add-ons, but addresses from &H300 to &H31F are often available.

It is acceptable to use any vacant input/output addresses in the upper half of the PC's input/output map. However, bear in mind that addresses that are free on your PC might not be available on other PCs.

Although there is a large number of lines available on an ISA expansion slot, relatively few of these are needed in order to undertake some simple

PC interfacing.

Modern PCs are essentially "turbo" AT class PCs, and interfacing to an ISA slot is much the same whether you have an old PC or a modern one. In fact, eight-bit interfacing is much the same whether you are using an original PC or a modern one with a gigahertz plus processor. An ISA bus is slowed down to an effective operating frequency of about 8MHz.

The parallel and serial ports of a PC represent the easiest method of interfacing your own circuits to a PC, and these are the best starting point. Practically any gadget can be interfaced to a PC via one or other of these ports.

MS-DOS programming languages are the most accommodating when you need to directly access the input/output ports. However, these languages are crude in comparison to most Windows programming languages. Some Windows based languages have the ability to directly access ports, and this ability can often be added to those that lack a built-in facility of this type.

Windows 95, 98 and ME are preferable to Windows NT, 2000, and XP when using a PC with your own add-on circuits. There is no problem with direct port access using the Windows 9x operating systems, but it is not permitted using Windows NT4, etc.

ISA bus interfacing

Decoding

When designing ISA interface circuits the first task is to produce a suitable address decoder circuit. Although circuits of this type are generally called address decoders, in most cases they also need to decode a few lines of the control bus as well. When you access one of your add-on circuits a certain set of logic states appear on the address bus, and on certain lines of the control bus. This set of logic states should be unique to that particular add-on, and should not occur when any other circuit is being accessed. The purpose of the address decoder is to recognise this set of logic states, and to produce a change in logic level at its output while that set of logic levels persists. The output of the address decoder normally holds the data bus of the add-on circuit in an inactive state. However, when it detects the appropriate combination of input levels its change in output state activates the add-on circuit.

Bus times

The basic way in which the add-on responds depends on whether it is a "read" or a "write" device. If the computer must read data from the circuit, once activated, the add-on's data bus will become a normal set of logic outputs. It is important to get things absolutely right with this type of circuit. If it should be activated at the wrong time, it will probably try to place data onto the data bus at the same time as some other piece of hardware. It might even try to place data onto the data bus at the same time as the microprocessor is writing data. Modern logic circuits are generally quite tolerant of this type of thing, and being realistic about it, the chances of anything being damaged are slight. On the other hand, it is clearly better not to risk any damage to expensive hardware, no matter how small the risk might be. Also, a data bus conflict of this type

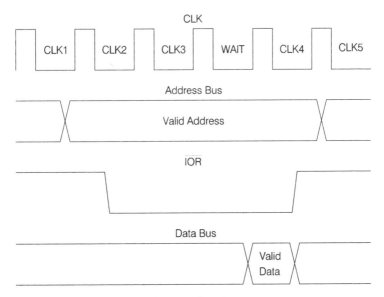

Fig.2.1 The ISA bus timing for a read cycle

is almost certain to crash the computer. Continuously rebooting a crashed computer is a good way to waste a lot of time, as many users of modern PCs will testify!

It is also important for things to be just right when writing data to an add-on circuit. The situation is slightly less critical in that when an add-on of this type is activated it reads whatever is on the data bus. If it is activated at the wrong time it will increase the loading on the data bus, but this is not likely to cause any ill effects. The data read by the device will be erroneous though, and the add-on will totally fail to function. A device that only reads from the data bus can obviously not try to force data onto the bus, and in theory at any rate, can not cause any damage or even crash the computer.

Read cycle

Figure 2.1 shows bus timing for a read cycle. The correct address is placed on the address bus some time before valid data from the peripheral circuit must be ready and waiting on the data bus, so that it can be read by the microprocessor. Similarly, -IOR goes low well before data is present on the data bus. This gives time for the address decoder to operate and

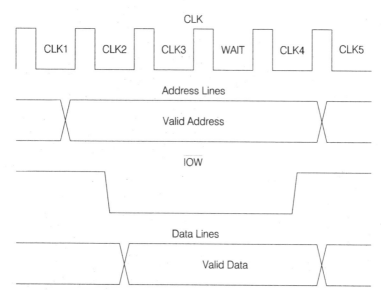

Fig.2.2 The ISA bus timing for a write cycle

provide an active output level. The timing for a write cycle is shown in Figure 2.2. The main point to note here is that -IOW returns to the high state while valid data is still being placed onto the data bus. This causes the active output signal from the address decoder to cease, and it is this transition which is used to latch the data

In normal logic circuit terms the address decoder does not need to be particularly fast in operation. The more advanced PCs of today operate at clock rates that are high by the standards of normal logic devices, with most now into the gigahertz range. However, the ISA bus is not especially fast in general electronic terms, even on the fastest PCs. So-called wait states are added when the ISA bus is accessed, slowing it to an effective clock rate of only about 8MHz. On the other hand, the address decoder has nanoseconds rather than microseconds in which to work.

Ordinary CMOS integrated circuits are not suitable as they are too slow. These components are designed for low current consumption, which is achieved at the expense of very sluggish performance. In any case, these components are not logic compatible with the PC buses. The buses of a PC operate at normal TTL levels. Ordinary 74** series devices are unsuitable as they load the buses too heavily. 74LS** series integrated circuits are well suited to this application as they are both fast and load the buses by acceptable amounts. 74HCT** components are also suitable, but the 74HC** components are not. The 74HC** logic devices operate at CMOS rather than TTL logic levels.

Practical decoding

Here we will only be concerned with decoders for use in the prototype card address range of &H300 to &H31F. The general principles discussed here apply to interfacing using other address ranges, but obviously the address line states that have to be decoded will be different if another address range is used. As pointed out previously, it is unlikely that it would ever be necessary to use other address ranges, since the 32 available addresses from &H300 to &H31F will be sufficient for most needs. It should only be necessary to use a different address range if &H300 to &H31F is already occupied and there is definitely no way of freeing it. It is probably best not to attempt to use other address ranges unless you are absolutely sure you know what you are doing.

If we first consider matters in fairly broad terms, the minimal address decoding needed is to decode address lines A5 to A9. Additionally, AEN must be decoded, together with -IOR and (or) -IOW. These are the states of these lines when an input address in the range &H300 to &H31F is accessed.

Line	Logic State
A5	Low
A6	Low
A7	Low
A8	High
A9	High
AEN	Low
-IOR	Low
-IOW	High

For read operations the state of -IOW is irrelevant, and it does not need to be decoded. This gives us the basic read address decoder represented diagrammatically in Figure 2.3. This will respond to any read operation to an input device in the address range &H300 to &H31F, but it should ignore any other read operations, as well as all write types and memory accesses. Most decoders are designed to have an output that is normally high and which goes low when the circuit is activated. Not all peripheral

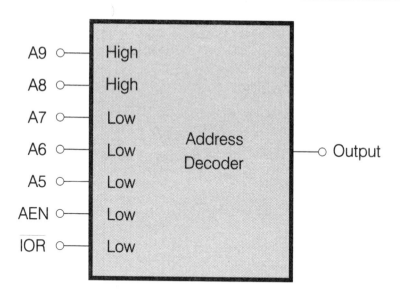

Fig.2.3 The most basic of "read" address decoders. This will respond to any address from &H300 to &H31F

circuits require things this way round though, and where appropriate the decoder must be designed to have an output that is normally low, and which pulses high while it is activated. Remember that in order to convert a decoder from one type to the other you merely need to add an inverter at the output.

This is the set of states that must be decoded when an output circuit in the relevant address range is accessed.

Line	Logic State
A5	Low
A6	Low
A7	Low
A8	High
A9	High
AEN	Low
-IOR	High
-IOW	Low

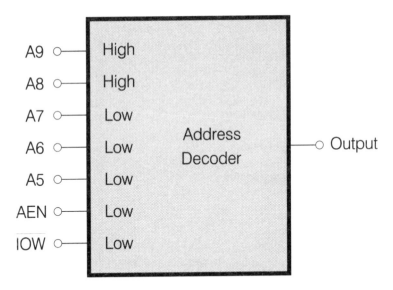

Fig.2.4 The "write" equivalent of Fig.2.3

This is the same as before, but the states of -IOR and -IOW have been reversed. In this case it is -IOR that can be ignored and -IOW that must be decoded. This basic "write" decoder is shown diagrammatically in Figure 2.4. When designing any address decoder or similar logic circuits it is a good idea to write down the decoded state of each line, or produce a diagram of the type shown in Figure 2.4, so that you get a clear picture of what is required. This can help to avoid time-consuming errors.

Read/write

In practice you will not always need an address decoder specifically for a read circuit or a write type. Most practical interfacing applications involve both reading and writing to the peripheral circuit. Even if the purpose of a port is (say) to output eight-bit bytes of data, it may well consist of more than just eight output lines. It is often necessary to carefully control the flow of data from the basic eight-bit port to some further hardware. This requires one or more handshake lines, one of which will probably be an input to monitor the status of the secondary piece of hardware.

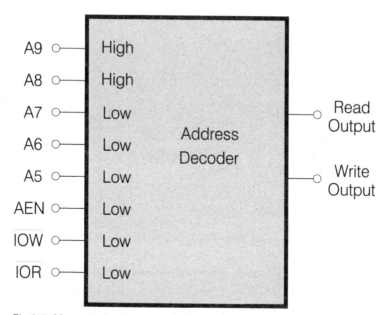

Fig.2.5 Many applications require an address decoder that provides
"read" and "write" outputs

A Centronics type parallel printer port is a good example of an eight-bit
output port of this type. It includes a strobe output that provides a pulse
each time a fresh byte of data is placed on the data outputs. It has two
handshake inputs ("Acknowledge" and "Busy"), one of which is used to
indicate whether or not the printer is ready to receive further data. The
correct flow of data into or out of the computer is something you need to
consider carefully when undertaking do-it-yourself interfacing. Get this
aspect of things slightly wrong, and you may well find yourself having to
do a complete redesign and rebuilding job on the add-on card.

One way of tackling the problem of combined read and write address
decoding is to produce two separate address decoders, one for each
function. This has to be regarded as doing things the hard way, and is
also not a strictly valid method of PC interfacing. Each line of the PC
expansion bus should be loaded by no more than one 74LS** series
TTL input, or an equivalent amount. Using two address decoders would
load some lines with two inputs. In practice this would probably not
matter too much, and there are ways around the problem. One of these
is to add buffers on the relevant lines so that these limit the loading of the

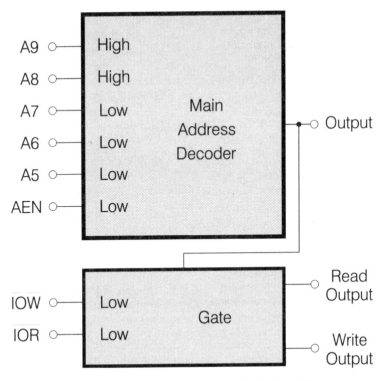

Fig.2.6 A simple but effective method of read/write decoding

bus lines to one 74LS** TTL load. This further adds to the complication and expense of the address decoder though.

All in one

In general it is better to produce an all-in-one address decoder of the type depicted in Figure 2.5. With AEN and the five address inputs at the appropriate states, the "Read" output is activated if -IOR is low, and the "Write" output is activated if -IOW is low. While it is quite possible to produce a decoder of this type, in practice it is often easier to have a decoder that does not process -IOR or -IOW. The output of this simple decoder is then fed to a further decoder, which does process -IOW and -IOR. This scheme of things is shown in Figure 2.6. The gate circuit, which generates the separate "Read" and "Write" outputs, can be very simple indeed. This system is very versatile in that it also provides a combined "read/write" output, which is what is needed for some peripheral chips. This type of decoder is therefore apposite to just about any method of interfacing.

The interface chips that require a combined "read/write" decoder output are the 82** series which are specifically designed for operation with 8080 series microprocessors. There are actually a number of other peripheral chips that are designed to be bus compatible with the 8080 series of microprocessors. These are less common than the 82** series chips, but you may well encounter some devices of this type. These chips are all used in the manner shown in Figure 2.7. The address decoder only has to process AEN plus address lines A5 to A9. -IOR and -IOW are not simply ignored, but are instead decoded by the appropriate inputs of the 82** series integrated circuit.

Precise decoding

So far we have only considered the situation where a single input register and one output register are to be used. The address decoder has treated the &H300 to &H31F address range as if it was a single address. The peripheral circuit effectively occupies all these addresses, and can be operated using any address in this range. This means that no other devices can exist in this address range, which is obviously a bit restrictive. With many of the 82** series chips there are several registers, and each chip must therefore occupy several addresses, with a different register located at each address.

This is easily accomplished, as the 82** series integrated circuits, which have more than one read/write register, have one or more register select inputs. These are simply fed from the address bus, and would normally be fed from the least significant address lines (i.e. A0, A1, etc.). In the example set-up of Figure 2.7 there are three register select inputs which are fed from address lines A0 to A2. The table on the next page shows the number of registers available for various numbers of chip select inputs.

No. Of C/S Inputs	Maximum No. Of Registers
0	1
1	2
2	4
3	8
4	16

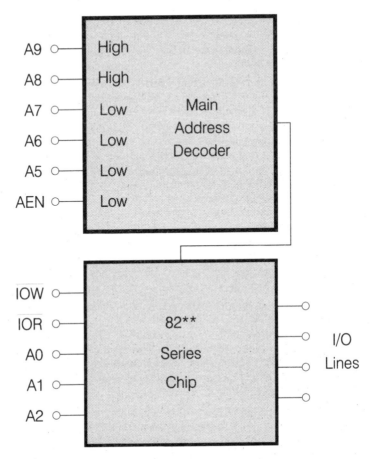

Fig.2.7 The basic scheme of things when using 82**, etc. chips

In the example of Figure 2.7 there are three chip select inputs fed from three address lines. This gives a maximum of eight read registers and eight write types. These registers are at addresses from &H300 to &H308. However, as less than full address decoding is being used, with A3 and A4 being left unprocessed, the full range of 32 addresses remain occupied. The eight registers appear again as an echo at addresses &H309 to &H30F. There are further echoes at &H310 to &H318, and &H319 to &H31F. This blocks any further add-ons being used in the &H300 to &H31F address range.

Two 82** series peripheral chips can be used in a set-up of the type shown in Figure 2.8. The two chips are connected to the expansion bus in parallel. We are ignoring the data bus in these address-decoding examples, but these would both be connected to the data bus of the expansion bus. The address decoder has two outputs, one for each peripheral chip. These outputs cover different address ranges. In practice this can only be achieved by processing further address lines.

Conventionally, it would be address line A4 that was decoded. One peripheral would be activated when A4 was high, the other would be activated when it was low. This would put the first peripheral device (A4 low) at addresses from &H300 to &H308, and at echoes from &H309 to &H30F. The second peripheral (A4 high) would be at addresses from &H310 to &H318, and at echoes from &H319 to &H31F. By also decoding A3 it would be possible to have four chips. The two extra chips would occupy the address ranges that were previously occupied by echoes. More than four chips having eight registers would not be possible, as this would require more than the available 32 addresses. As pointed out previously, there are ways of obtaining greater expansion, but it is unlikely that more than 32 read registers and 32 write types would be needed.

One slight flaw with this method of using devices in parallel is that some lines of the expansion bus are loaded by more than one input. In particular, the data bus will be loaded by several inputs. This does not necessarily matter in practice, since there should only be one input in the active state at any one time. The loading is therefore much less than it might at first appear. However, in this sort of situation you can always play safe by including buffers on the lines which might otherwise be excessively loaded.

Gates AND decoders

There is no single solution to address decoding problems, and there are often dozens of different ways of achieving much the same thing. Some solutions are more practical than others. In general, it is better to use simple gates and inverters. These are fast in operation and inexpensive. They do sometimes have a disadvantage, which is that it can take a lot of inter-wiring in order to get a few gates and inverters to give the desired action. For a home constructed unit it may sometimes be better to opt for more complex devices, such as three to eight line decoders, in order to keep the board layout reasonably simple and straightforward. The more complex decoder integrated circuits can be quite expensive, and are often relatively slow in operation. These may actually be perfectly usable for PC address decoding, but it should be possible to find good

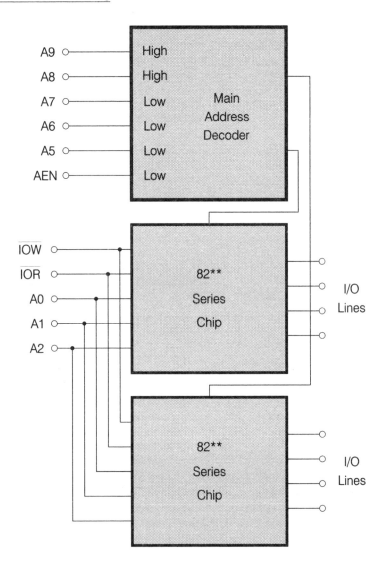

Fig.2.8 Using more than one peripheral device. In reality at least one more line is decoded

ways of handling the decoding without resorting to any of the more exotic 74LS** series of integrated circuits.

The two basic types of logic gate are the AND and OR varieties. Logic gates all have two or more inputs, and a single output. If we consider a simple two-input AND gate first, the truth table provided below shows the function it performs:

INPUT 1	INPUT 2	OUTPUT
Low	Low	Low
Low	High	Low
High	Low	Low
High	High	High

Its output is low unless input 1 AND input 2 are high, and it is from this that the AND name is derived. The action is much the same if there are more inputs. With all the inputs high, the output is high. If one or more of the inputs are low, the output is low. This is the truth table for a two-input OR gate:

INPUT 1	INPUT 2	OUTPUT
Low	Low	Low
Low	High	High
High	Low	High
High	High	High

The output of a two-input OR gate is low unless one OR other of its inputs is high, and it is from this that the OR name is derived. Again, the action of the gate remains much the same if there are more than two inputs. With none of the inputs in the high state the output will be low, but if one or more of the inputs should go high, the output will also go high.

There are couple of variations on the AND and OR gates, and these are called NAND and NOR gates. These are the truth tables for two-input NAND and NOR gates respectively:

INPUT 1	INPUT 2	OUTPUT
Low	Low	High
Low	High	High
High	Low	High
High	High	Low

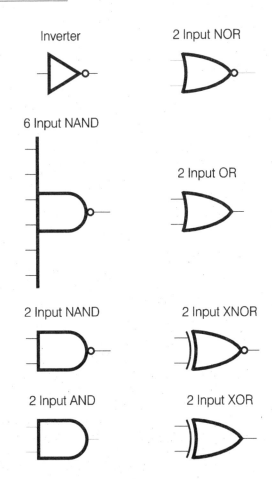

Fig.2.9 Gate and inverter circuit symbols

INPUT 1	INPUT 2	OUTPUT
Low	Low	High
Low	High	Low
High	Low	Low
High	High	Low

These really only differ from the original truth tables in that the output states are reversed. In effect, a NAND gate is an AND gate with its output fed through an inverter. Therefore, if input 1 and input 2 are taken high, the output goes low. Any other set of input states sends the output high. Similarly, a NOR gate is effectively just an OR gate with its output inverted.

There is actually a fifth type of gate, but this is little used in practice. It is the exclusive OR (XOR) gate, which is similar to an OR gate. However, with an OR gate, the output is not simply high if input 1 or input 2 is high. If both inputs are taken to the high state, then the output will still go high. With an exclusive OR gate taking just one input high will send the output high. Having no inputs set high, or more than one input set to the high state, results in the output going low. I suppose that this could reasonably be regarded as the true OR gate action, but in practice it tends to be less useful that the conventional OR gate action, and exclusive OR gates are something of a rarity. There are also exclusive NOR gates and these are effectively just an exclusive OR gate with an inverter at the output.

Figure 2.9 shows the circuit symbols for the various types of two input gate. It also shows the circuit symbols for an inverter and a multi-input (NAND) gate. Note that gate circuit symbols seem to be less rigidly standardised than most other circuit symbols, and that you may well encounter different gate symbols in other publications. However, it is usually fairly obvious what type of gate each symbol is meant to depict.

Of the various decoder chips available the 74LS138 is probably the most useful low cost type for address decoding purposes. Pinout details for this 16-pin DIL chip are shown in Figure 2.10. It is a three to eight line decoder, and it has outputs that are normally high. One of the outputs goes to the low state, and which output this is depends on the binary pattern fed to the three inputs. This table shows which set of input states activates each output.

INPUT 0	INPUT 1	INPUT 2	OUTPUT
Low	Low	Low	0
Low	Low	High	1
Low	High	Low	2
Low	High	High	3
High	Low	Low	4
High	Low	High	5
High	High	Low	6
High	High	High	7

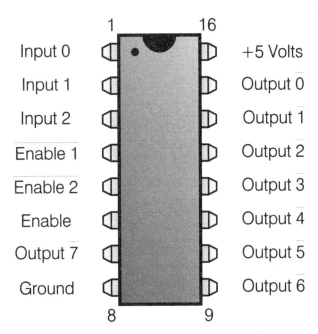

Fig.2.10 Pinout details for the 74LS138. This is one of the most useful chips for address decoding

The 74LS138 is rather more useful than it might at first appear. The first point to note is that there are three further inputs. In most cases it is not limited to decoding three lines, and can actually decode up to six lines. The additional three lines are "enable" types, and unless they are taken to the appropriate state, the outputs of the device all go to the third logic state. In other words they simply go to a high impedance state, and will not drive logic inputs. The inputs at pins 4 and 5 are negative enable inputs, and they must be taken to logic 0 in order to make the device function normally. The enable input at pin 6 is a positive type, and this pin must be taken high in order to produce normal operation of the chip.

The second point to note is that different sets of input states activate different outputs of the 74LS138. This gives the potential of having the device decode several blocks of addresses, with each block having its own output. Even if you do not require several decoded outputs on one card, it is possible to standardise on the same decoder circuit for several cards, with a different output being used on each card. You could, for

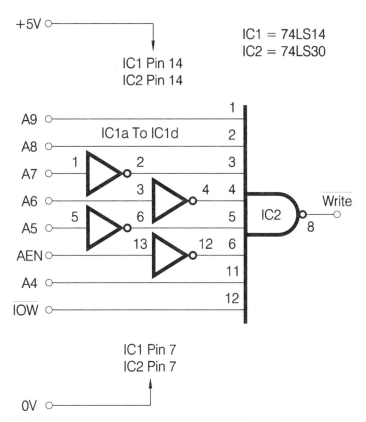

Fig.2.11 A simple decoder using inverters and a NAND gate

example, have the &H300 to &H31F address range split into four blocks of eight addresses, with each block activating a different output of the 74LS138. You could then have up to four do-it-yourself expansion cards using the same basic address decoder circuit, provided each card utilized a different output of its address decoder.

Decoder circuits

A popular method of PC address decoding is to have a decoder circuit based on a 74LS30 eight input NAND gate. This has an output that goes low if all eight inputs are high, or high if any of the inputs are low. Obviously

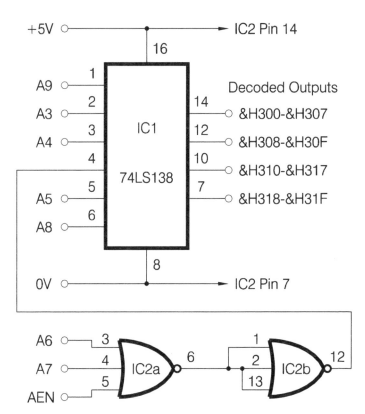

Fig.2.12 A simple but versatile PC address decoder. IC2 is a 74LS27
         triple 3-input NOR gate

you will not need a PC address decoder that decodes eight lines to the
high state. Typically the requirement is for something more like a decoder
which is activated by four lines high and four lines low. The simple way
around this problem is to feed to the 74LS30 via inverters any lines that
must be decoded to the low state.

Figure 2.11 shows a typical address decoder based on a 74LS30 eight-
input NAND gate plus some inverters. In this case there are four inverters,
and these are part of a 74LS14 hex Schmitt trigger/inverter package.
However, this general scheme of things should work properly using any
74LS** series inverters. This decoder is designed to act as a "Write"
decoder. It decodes A4, A8, and A9 to the high state and A5 to A7 to the

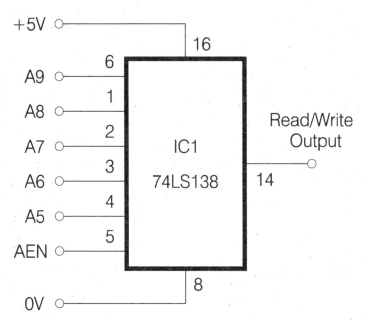

+5V

A9   6

A8   1

A7   2

A6   3

A5   4

AEN   5

16

IC1

74LS138

Read/Write
Output

14

8

0V

Fig.2.13 A simple PC address decoder that lacks versatility

low state. This means that it will be activated when any address from
&H310 to &H31F is accessed for a write operation. If A4 was to be fed to
IC2 via an inverter, it would then be decoded to the low state, and the
circuit would be activated by write operations to addresses from &H300
to &H30F. Connect -IOR instead of -IOW, and the decoder will then act
as a read type.

This type of address decoder is very cheap and simple, but as pointed
out previously, it can be a bit awkward when it comes to actually building
the circuit. It is also slightly lacking in versatility. Figure 2.12 shows the
circuit diagram for a PC address decoder based on a 74LS138. This is
still pretty cheap and simple, but it is much more versatile than the circuit
based on the 74LS30.

A minimalist PC address decoder would have to decode address lines
from A5 to A9, plus AEN and possibly -IOR or -IOW. It is just possible to
do this using a 74LS138, with the only proviso that any decoding of -IOR
or -IOW must be provided separately. Figure 2.13 shows the circuit for a
minimalist address decoder of this type, and I suppose this could be
used if you only wanted to have (say) one 8255 parallel interface chip in

the &H300 to &H31F address space. However, by using a very simple address decoder of this type you would be painting yourself into the proverbial corner, and it would be difficult to add more user add-ons at a later date.

The circuit of Figure 2.12 offers much greater versatility, but it requires the use of an extra chip. This is a 74LS27 triple three-input NOR gate. In this circuit only two of the gates are required, and no connections are made to the third gate. IC2b is simply wired as an inverter, and it effectively converts IC2a into a three-input OR gate. It might seem to be easier to simply use a three-input OR gate, but a suitable device seems to be difficult to obtain. The 74LS27 is widely available, and is easily wired to give the required circuit action.

This arrangement enables three lines to drive one input of the 74LS138, permitting a maximum of eight rather than six lines to be decoded. A6, A7, and AEN are decoded to the low state by the gates and one of the low enable inputs of IC1. The other low enable input decodes A5, while the high enable input decodes A8. A9 is fed to input 0, and it is effectively decoded to the high state. This renders four of IC1's eight outputs effectively inoperative. Inputs 1 and 2 of IC1 decode A3 and A4, and the states on these lines, when all the other decoded lines are at the appropriate logic levels, dictates which of the four outputs of IC1 is activated. In other words, the &H300 to &H31F address range is divided into four blocks of eight addresses. Figure 2.12 shows the range of addresses that activates each output.

If you only wanted two blocks of sixteen addresses, then A3 would not be decoded, and instead, pin 2 of IC1 would be connected to the 0-volt supply rail. The output at pin 14 would then be activated by addresses from &H300 to &H30F, and the output at pin 10 would be activated by addresses from &H310 to &H31F. Obviously more address decoding can be added if more but smaller blocks of addresses are needed. This can be accomplished using another gate or gates ahead of one or more of IC1's inputs. This would enable A9 to be decoded elsewhere, leaving input 0 (pin 1) of IC1 free to decode A2. All eight outputs of IC1 would then be brought into action. However, for most purposes the address decoder of Figure 2.12 will suffice without resorting to any modifications. Blocks of eight addresses are sufficient to accommodate most add-ons, while four blocks should give enough scope for expansion. With one address block per add-on card, this would be sufficient to use up all the expansion slots in most computers.

As already pointed out, with some peripheral chips there is no need to bother about decoding -IOW and -IOR, since some chips provide inputs

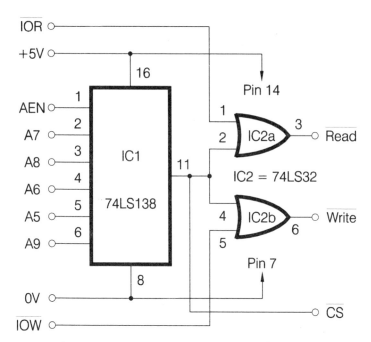

Fig.2.14 Producing separate outputs for read and write circuits

for these lines and do the necessary decoding. This is not always the case though, and when using circuits that are wholly or largely based on TTL logic chips, you will normally have to decode -IOR and -IOW. Figure 2.14 shows a simple PC address decoder and the additional circuitry needed in order to produce separate read and write output signals. This basically just consists of processing the -IOW line and the output of the decoder using a two-input OR gate.

During a write operation to the appropriate address range, both of these lines will go low, and so will the output of the gate. Essentially the same system is used with a second OR gate to process the -IOR line and produce a read output. A negative chip select output is still available from the basic address decoder circuit, and can be used with any chips that have built-in processing for -IOW and -IOR. Note that this method of gating should work perfectly well with any address decoder circuit, but only if it provides negative output pulses.

Parallel I/O ports

In order to produce an eight-bit output port all that is needed is an address decoder plus an eight-bit latch. Simply using something like a tristate eight-bit buffer to provide an output port is not usually acceptable. This would only provide a valid output for the duration that the data bus was fed through to the outputs. This is likely to be well under a microsecond in practice. What is needed is a circuit that will latch this momentary flash of data, so that the outputs can be used to drive relays, l.e.d.s, digital to analogue converters, or whatever. The situation is generally somewhat different when it comes to inputting data. You normally have a set of what are essentially static input levels, and these must be fed through to the data bus while the port is read. An eight-bit tristate buffer is all that is needed to achieve this.

Figure 2.15 shows the circuit diagram for a basic PC eight-bit input/output port. This is basically the same sort of circuit that has been used with numerous eight-bit home computers over the years, and it seems to work reliably with most PCs. Note that this circuit must be used in conjunction with a suitable address decoder circuit. This must be a decoder that includes the extra decoding to provide separate read and write outputs.

It is also worth noting that although no supply decoupling capacitors are featured in any of the circuits in this book, these must be included on any PC expansion cards. These are merely ceramic capacitors of about 100 nanofarads in value connected across the supply lines. Some circuit designers use one capacitor per TTL integrated circuit, with each capacitor mounted as close as possible to its respective integrated circuit. However, this is probably using a certain amount of over-kill, and one decoupling capacitor per three TTL integrated circuits (or other logic chips) should suffice.

The eight-bit output port of Figure 2.15 is provided by a 74LS273 octal D type flip/flop. The data bus connects to its D (data) inputs, and the latching output lines are provided by the Q outputs. These are non-inverting outputs which latch at whatever states are present on the D inputs when there is a positive transition on the CP (clock pulse) input. This transition is, of course, provided by the trailing edge of the write pulse from the address decoder.

The input port is provided by a 74LS245 octal transceiver (IC4). Conventionally an octal tristate buffer such as a 74LS244 is used in applications of this type. I prefer to use the 74LS245 simply because its

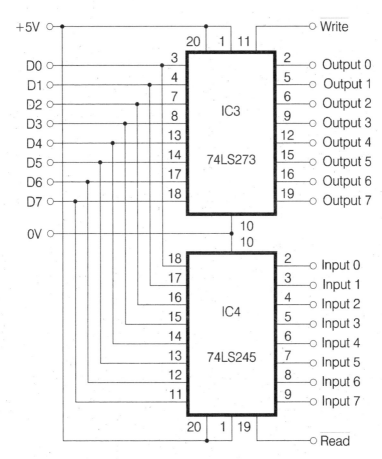

Fig.2.15 A simple PC 8-bit input/output port. Note that this requires an address decoder circuit in order to function properly

pinout arrangement is a more convenient one which helps to keep board layouts more simple and straightforward. In this case IC4 has pin 1 wired to the +5 volt supply so that it is permanently in the "send" mode. Its tristate outputs are controlled by the negative chip enable input at pin 19. When a negative pulse is received from the read output of the address decoder, the outputs are activated and the eight-bit input code is fed through to the PC's data bus.

The 8255

The standard parallel interface chip for the PCs (and many other computers come to that) is the 8255. This is bus compatible with the 8080 and 8086 series of microprocessors, and with the Z80 series. The Z80A microprocessor has been used in several popular eight-bit home computers, and the 8255 was popular in user add-ons for these machines. This chip may well be familiar to many readers, but it will be described in reasonable detail for the benefit of those who have not encountered it previously.

It is a 40-pin DIL chip, which provides three eight-bit input/output ports. This is one eight-bit port more than many parallel interface adapter chips, such as the 6522 and 6821. However, it is not quite as good as it may at first appear. Whereas chips such as the 6522 only provide two eight-bit ports, they also provide two handshake lines per port. These handshake lines are sufficiently versatile to accommodate any normal handshaking arrangements. This enables the two eight-bit ports to operate properly in any normal situations, including those where controlling the flow of data into or out of the port is critical and difficult.

By contrast, the ports of the 8255 have no handshake lines at all. Instead, where handshaking is needed, port C is split into two four-bit ports. One nibble is set as outputs while the other nibble is set as inputs, and these act as the handshake lines for Ports A and B. Thus, if you need eight-bit ports plus handshake lines, you only have two ports, plus (probably) a few leftover input and output lines from port C. If you require just basic input or output ports with no handshaking, then the 8255 has more to offer than most other parallel interface adapters. On the other hand, if you do require handshaking it is of little advantage. Although it might provide a few spare lines on port C, it is probably slightly less convenient to use than most other parallel port chips.

Block control

It is only fair to point out another relative shortcoming of the 8255, which is a lack of individual control over the functions of its input/output lines. With devices such as the 6522 and 6821 there is a data direction register for each port. By way of this register it is possible to set each line as an input or an output, as desired. If you require a port to have five lines as outputs to control relay drivers, and three as inputs to read sensor switches, then this is perfectly possible. You have full control over which lines are used as the inputs and which are set as the outputs. With the

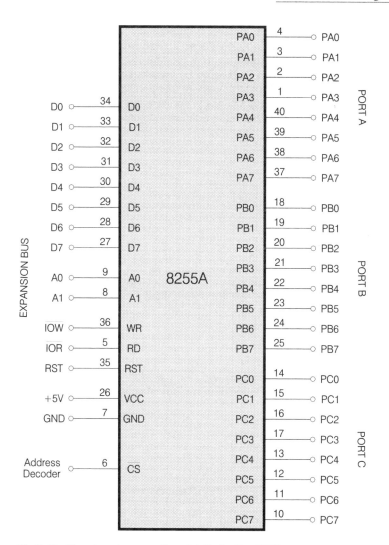

Fig.2.16 Pinout and connection details for the 8255

8255 all eight lines of a port must be set as outputs, or all eight must be set as inputs. The only exception to this is port C. As explained previously, this can be set for simple split operation (four lines as inputs and four lines as outputs).

Figure 2.16 gives pinout details for the 8255, and it also shows the correct method of connecting it to the PC expansion bus. The negative chip select input (pin 6) is fed from the address decoder, which must obviously be a type that provides negative output pulses (as do the address decoder circuits featured earlier in this chapter). The RST, -IOW, and -IOR lines of the control bus all connect to corresponding terminals of the 8255, as does the eight-bit data bus. There are two register select inputs on the 8255, which would normally connect to A0 and A1. Accordingly, they are called A0 and A1 rather than RS0 and RS1 (or something similar). If the address decoder responds (say) to eight addresses from &H308 to &H30F, then the 8255 will occupy four addresses from &H308 to &H30B. It will also occupy addresses from &H30C to &H30F in the form of one set of echoes. Therefore, these addresses would be unusable for other purposes. Of course, the 8255 could be placed in just four addresses with no echoes, but in most cases there will not be a great enough shortage of address space to make this worthwhile.

The outputs of the 8255 are latching types, and are compatible with 74LS** and 74HCT** TTL devices. The inputs are also compatible with these devices. In fact the device will work reliably with most logic devices, including most CMOS types.

Although it might seem better to use simple TTL input and output ports for most applications, the 8255 tends to be a more popular choice. One reason for this is undoubtedly that it provides a reasonably simple and inexpensive means of providing a lot of input/output lines. Also, it is designed specifically for operation with microprocessors such as the 8088 and 80286, etc., and should operate very reliably with these. I have encountered one or two PCs that seem to be something less than 100% reliable when used with some simple TTL output ports, especially when operating at higher bus speeds. I have never experienced any problems when using the 8255 though, regardless of the bus speed. I therefore tend to use it as my standard method of interfacing the PC expansion bus to digital to analogue converters, speech chips, or whatever.

8255 programming

There is insufficient space available here to go into great detail about all the 8255 operating modes, and methods of using this device. Anyone using practically any computer peripheral chip would be well advised to obtain the relevant data sheet, and I would certainly recommend this for anyone who is going to use a chip as complex as the 8255. However, here we will consider the basic ways of using this interface chip, which should at least get you started, and may be all that you need in order to use the chip effectively in your particular applications.

The 8255 has four read/write registers. Three of these are ports A, B, and C. Obviously each one of these would normally be used only as a read register or a write type, depending on whether its port has been set as an input or an output type. The exception to this is when port C is used in the split mode of operation, and it is then a form of read/write register. The fourth register is a control type, and data would normally only be written to this. You can read data from this register, but it will not furnish anything meaningful. If you need a record of what has been written to the control register, a byte of RAM must be used to store a copy of each control number that is written to this register. If we assume that the 8255 is at the example address range mentioned earlier (&H308 to &H30B), then the base addresses of the four registers would be as follows:-

HEX ADDRESS	DEC. ADDRESS	REGISTER
&H308	776	Port A
&H309	777	Port B
&H30A	778	Port C
&H30B	779	Control

Using the ports is straightforward enough, but the control register is a bit tricky to fully master. There are three modes of operation for the 8255, which have been designated modes 0, 1, and 2. Mode 0 is the most simple, and is the one you should use when initially experimenting with the 8255. In this mode the ports operate as simple input/output types, with the only complication that port C can operate in the split mode (one nibble as inputs and the other nibble as outputs).

Bits five to seven of the control register set the required operating mode. Bit seven is set high in order to enable the operating mode to be changed. Be careful to set this bit high, as the control register operates in a totally different manner if this bit is set to zero. Bits five and six control the operating mode. This table shows how this scheme of things operates.

MODE	BIT 7	BIT 6	BIT 5
0	1	0	0
1	1	0	1
2	1	1	0
2	1	1	1

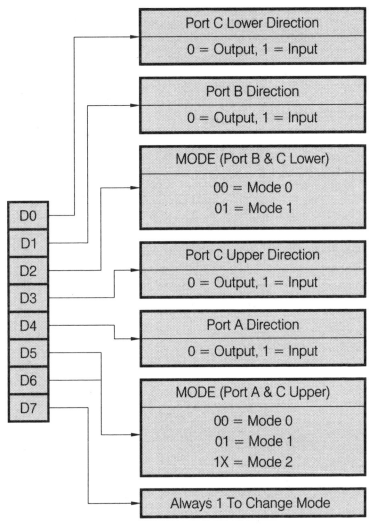

Fig.2.17 The functions of the bits in the 8255 control register

As will be apparent from this table, there are two control codes which select mode 2. It does not matter which one you use, the effect on the 8255 is exactly the same. These bits only control the mode of port A and the upper nibble of port C. Port B and the lower nibble of port C are controlled by bit 2 of the control register. This is either high for mode 1 operation, or low if you require mode 0 operation. Mode 2 is not applicable to these ports, and so one bit is all that is needed for their mode control.

Bits zero, one, three, and four are used to control the functions of the ports (i.e. whether they operate as inputs or outputs). This operates in the following manner.

PORT	CONTROL BIT	DEC. VALUE WHEN HIGH
0	C Lower	1
1	B	2
3	C Upper	8
4	A	16

In order to set a port as an output type the control bit is set to zero. Setting a control bit to 1 obviously sets its respective port as an input type. Those who are used to the 6522, 6821, etc., should note that this works the opposite way round to the data direction registers of these chips.

When writing to the control register you must set the mode of operation and the port directions in a single write operation. You can not write to bits five to seven first and then bits zero, one, three, and four. However, working out the right control register values is not difficult. For mode 0 operation bits five and six are low, and bit seven is high. To set bit seven high a decimal value of 128 is required. The table provided previously shows the decimal value needed for each control bit when it is set high (i.e. when its port is to be set as an input). A value of zero is, of course, needed for any bits that will be set low.

Simply take the values given in the table for the ports that are to be set as inputs, and add 128 to the total of these values. You then have the value to write to the control register. For Example, assume that port A and both nibbles of port C are to be set as inputs. The values for these ports as inputs are sixteen, eight, and one. This gives a total of 25. Adding 128 to this gives a grand total of 153, which is the value that must be written to the control register. In GW BASIC, and using the example port addresses mentioned previously, this value would be written to the control register using the instruction:

OUT 779,153

You can use hexadecimal addresses with GW BASIC if you prefer, but remember that hexadecimal numbers are indicated using both the "&H" prefix, not just the "&" prefix used in some languages. Numbers having just the "&" prefix may well be accepted, as I think that these are interpreted by GW BASIC as octal (base eight) numbers. This has led me into some time-consuming errors in the past as I tend to use just the "&" prefix from force of habit (having mainly used a BBC computer for interfacing in the past). Consequently, I now always use decimal input/ output addresses when using GW BASIC.

Mode 0

For many purposes mode 0 operation will suffice. For example, there are many applications that do not require any form of handshaking. These include such things as driving digital to analogue converters, relay drivers, etc., and reading simple sensors. For applications of this type you only need simple input and output lines, and there is no point in using anything beyond mode 0. Where handshaking is needed, setting port C for split operation to provide the handshake input/output lines will often suffice. This does not provide edge-triggered inputs or anything of this type, but simple input and output lines will usually be sufficient. Remember that where necessary you can always use some external signal processing, such as a pulse stretcher or shortener, in order to make things more reliable. For instance, if an output is providing very brief pulses, a pulse stretcher might provide a signal which can be read more reliably, with no pulses passing undetected by the handshake input.

Mode 1

Where complex handshaking is needed it might be better to resort to mode 1 operation. This uses port A and port B as eight-bit input output ports, and six lines of port C to act as strobed handshake lines and interrupt control signals (three lines per port). Mode 2 provides strobed bidirectional operation through port A, with five lines of port C acting as what I suppose is a sort of control bus. This is not a mode that I have ever used, and it is presumably only needed for a few specialised applications. Anyway, to fully get to grips with the 8255 you really need to study the data sheet and then experiment a little.

Other 82** series devices interface to the PC buses in much the same way as the 8255. Devices that are bus compatible with the 82** series of peripheral chips should also interface to the PC expansion bus without difficulty. It is often possible to interface peripheral chips for one series of microprocessors to a microprocessor from a different range. For example, chips intended for the 6502 and similar microprocessors have been used successfully with the Z80 microprocessor. It is usually possible to overcome the differences between the control buses, but it can take a certain amount of experimentation to get things right. For example, where a peripheral chip has a combined read/write line, either -IOW or -IOR might provide a suitable signal. If not, then inverting one of these lines or feeding it through a monostable might produce the desired result. If a negative reset signal is needed, then feeding the PC's reset line via an inverter should give the desired result, or you can put a suitable reset generator circuit on the expansion card. Studying the timing diagrams in data sheets can steer you in the right direction, but in the end it comes down to the "suck it and see" approach.

Design example

Bear in mind that devices which are described as "microprocessor bus compatible", or something similar, might not be compatible with the PC's version of a microprocessor bus. While most microprocessor compatible devices can probably be interfaced direct to the PC buses successfully, this may not always be feasible. With some peripheral chips it is probably best not to attempt to interface them direct onto the PC expansion bus. You have to carefully assess each interfacing problem, and work out the most appropriate solution. When in doubt it is probably best to take the safer but more complex approach, and interface to the PC expansion bus indirectly via an 8255 (or whatever).

We will now consider a example of interfacing devices to the PC bus, in order to illustrate the problems that can arise and some possible solutions to them. We will use an analogue to digital converter as our design example as this is fairly typical in the interfacing problems it provides. The circuits described here can actually be used as the basis of your own projects, as we will be dealing with practical integrated circuits, not notional devices. The circuits have all been tried and tested.

Some devices are much easier to interface to the PC expansion bus than others, and the ADC0844 analogue to digital converter represents a relatively easy option. Pinout details for this device is shown in Figure 2.18. The ADC0844 is relatively easy to interface to a PC because it is specifically designed to interface to 8080 and 8088 type buses. This analogue to digital converter chip has an eight-bit data bus (DB0 to DB7) with tristate outputs. It can therefore output to the data bus by driving the chip select (-CS) input from a suitable address decoder circuit. There is no need for the address decoder to process -IOR or -IOW as there are inputs for these on the ADC0844 (-RD and -WR).

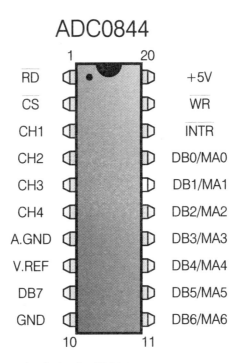

ADC0844

Fig.2.18 Pinout details for the ADC0844

You will notice from Figure 2.18 that the lower four bits of the address bus are labelled DB0/MA0 to DB3/MA3. This is due to the fact that these pins are dual purpose, and also operate as what the ADC0844 data sheet refers to as address inputs. This is perhaps not a strictly accurate way of looking at things since the chip only occupies a single address, and these pins do little more than switch between several internal registers. The basic method of using the ADC0844 is to first write to the device in order to start a conversion, and to then read it in order to extract the converted value. Sometimes with this type of thing the value written to the chip is simply a dummy value, and can be any legal value (i.e. any integer from 0 to 255). The ADC0844 is a fairly complex device though, and it has four analogue inputs. There is actually only one converter, but this is preceded by a four way multiplexer (an electronic switch) that can connect any one of these inputs through to the converter. The value written to the device determines which input is connected through to the converter.

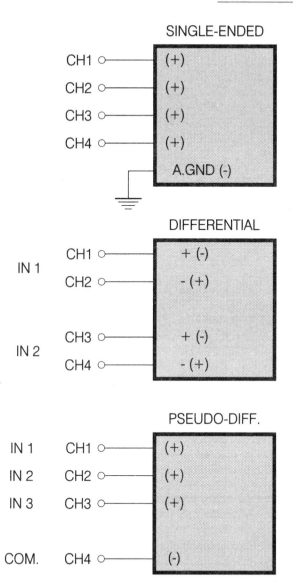

Fig.2.19 The input arrangements for the ADC0844's three modes

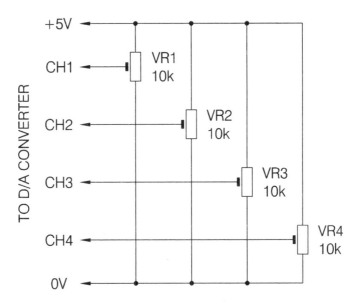

Fig.2.20 Using the ADC0844 in its ratiometric mode. The +5V supply is used as the reference voltage

Input modes

Matters are actually a bit more complicated than this, because there are three modes of operation available. The most simple of these is the single-ended mode, and with this there are four inputs. The voltage converted is the potential from the analogue ground pin to whichever input has been selected. In other words, this is the normal four-channel mode of the device. You will notice from Figure 2.18 that there are separate analogue and digital ground terminals. These do not necessarily have to be held at the same potential, but in most cases they would simply be wired together and connected to a common analogue/digital ground.

There are two differential modes available, and in the standard differential mode there are two inputs available. The first uses what would normally be the channel 1 and channel 2 inputs, while the second uses the channel 3 and channel 4 inputs. The other differential mode is a pseudo type, in which the channel 4 input acts as a common negative input, and the other three inputs respond to their voltage relative to the channel 4 input.

In other words, if you wish to measure voltages with respect to a potential other than the earth one, connect the channel 4 input to a suitable offset voltage, and then use inputs 1 to 3 to measure the voltages. Note that in the differential and pseudo differential modes the analogue ground terminal is not used as an input, but it would normally be connected to ground anyway. Figure 2.19 shows the available modes in diagrammatic form, and might help to clarify matters.

This table shows the values that must be written to the ADC0844 in order to select each of the available operating modes, and the options available within each mode (e.g. which channel is to be read). The table shows the polarity with which the input signals must be applied to the device.

CONT. VAL.	CH1	CH2	CH3	CH4	A.GND	MODE
0	+	-	X	X	X	Differential
1	-	+	X	X	X	Differential
2	X	X	+	-	X	Differential
3	X	X	-	+	X	Differential
4	+	X	X	X	-	Single-ended
5	X	+	X	X	-	Single-ended
6	X	X	+	X	-	Single-ended
7	X	X	X	+	-	Single-ended
12	+	X	X	-	X	Pseudo Diff.
13	X	+	X	-	X	Pseudo Diff.
14	X	X	+	-	X	Pseudo Diff.

Reference voltage

The reference voltage fed to the V.REF pin controls the full-range sensitivity of the device. The full-range value is achieved at whatever voltage is used as the reference potential. This voltage must be in the range 0 to 5 volts, but for good results it should not be much less than about 1 volt. For some purposes the reference voltage can simply be provided by the +5 volt supply, or can be a fraction of this supply obtained via a simple potential divider.

Neither method is particularly satisfactory in precision measurement applications because the +5 volt rail is not likely to be highly stable or noise-free. The stability of most PC +5 volt rails is not actually all that bad, but for a critical application such as using an analogue to digital converter for accurate measurements, very well stabilised reference voltages are often needed. One method of using the device, which avoids the need for a highly stable reference voltage, is the ratiometric method. This is where the input voltages are derived from potential dividers across the +5 volt supply, as in Figure 2.20. Although the potentiometers are shown as being presets in Figure 2.20, in reality they could be ordinary potentiometers, or even potential dividers having a fixed resistor for one element, and a thermistor or some other type of sensor as the other element. The +5 volt rail is used as the reference voltage.

The point about this method is that any change in the supply voltage will affect both the reference potential and the input potential. The two changes cancel out one another, giving no change in readings. Where a highly stable reference voltage is needed, any of the many low-voltage reference generator chips should be suitable. These give highly stable reference voltages, which have excellent temperature stability.

Conversion time

The -INTR pin is a status output. The conversion process is not an instant process, or even a particularly fast one. The ADC0844 is fairly average in terms of its conversion time, which is typically about 30μs at 25 degrees Celsius. Obviously data must not be read from the device prematurely, as invalid data would then be obtained. One method of avoiding this problem, and one which usually works well in practice, is to simply have a timing loop to provide a delay between issuing each start conversion signal and reading the converter. If necessary, some experimentation can be used in order to find the optimum delay time (i.e. the shortest delay which gives reliable operation). Bear in mind that if you are using a fairly slow computer language, such as an interpreted BASIC, you may well find that you can not read the device prematurely. With the speed of modern PCs this is by no means certain though, and delay loops are now often required in situations where they would have been unnecessary in the past.

An alternative to using a time delay is to have an input line to read the -INTR output. This is normally high, and goes low when a conversion has been completed. The hold-off would then be obtained by monitoring -INTR using a simple loop routine, and only permitting the converter to be read once -INTR had gone low. Incidentally, -INTR is reset automatically when the converter is read. There is a slight problem with this method in that an input line is required. If the analogue to digital

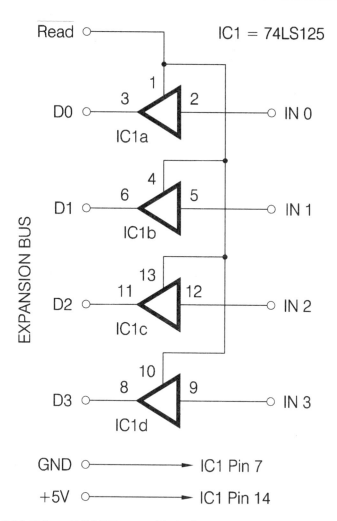

Fig.2.21 Using a 74LS125 to provide four inputs

converter is part of a large interface card, then there may well be a spare input somewhere that can be used. However, if it is on a simple ADC card, there will probably be no spare lines that can be used. Clearly, adding an 8255 in order to read one line would be using the proverbial "sledgehammer to crack a nut", and using a 74LS245 to provide one

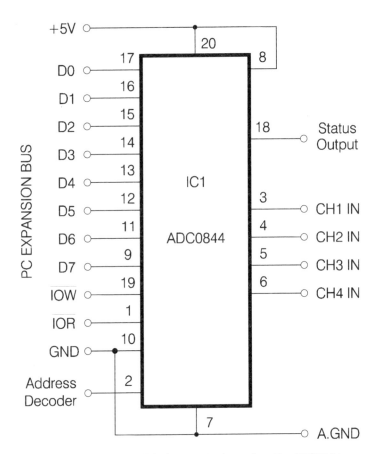

Fig.2.22 An analogue to digital converter based on the ADC0844

line would not be much better. A more practical approach is to use a device such as the 74LS125, which can provide up to four input lines. Figure 2.21 shows how this device can be used as a quad input port. Of course, if you only need one input line, you can use one of the buffers and ignore the other three. However, it is not a bad idea to implement all four lines, since the spare inputs might turn out to be useful for something.

There is a third option, which is to use the -INTR output to generate an interrupt. This is not difficult from the hardware point of view, but you need to be fairly expert at PC programming in order to handle this type of thing. In an application of this type it is not normally necessary to resort to using interrupts. It is only likely to be worthwhile doing so in applications that are processor intensive, and where it would therefore be unacceptable to have the processor idling away waiting for conversions to be completed. Few applications for analogue to digital converters fall into this category. Mostly a set of readings are read and stored in memory, and they are only processed once a full set has be gathered, and no more readings will be taken. In some cases readings are taken and immediately displayed on the screen, which is not usually very demanding on the microprocessor.

Figure 2.22 shows the circuit diagram for an analogue to digital converter based on the ADC0844, complete with details of the connections to the PC expansion bus. This circuit uses the +5 volt supply as the reference voltage. Remember that the address decoder should be a type that does not decode -IOR and -IOW, as these are dealt with by the ADC0844. This circuit does not utilize the -INTR status output, and my preference is to simply use a delay loop if there is a danger of taking readings too frequently.

One final point is that the ADC0844 usually has a suffix to the basic type number. The suffix indicates the case style and operating temperature range of the component. You are most likely to see the ADC0844CCN advertised in component catalogues, and this is the version I used. Any version of the device should be satisfactory for normal purposes though.

Finally

With the information provided here, anyone with a reasonable amount of experience at electronics construction should be able to interface a wide range of devices to the PC's ISA expansion bus without too much difficulty. PC interfacing is really very straightforward, and is actually much easier than interfacing to most of the eight-bit computers I have dealt with (which includes practically all the popular eight-bit machines). Complications can arise if wait states have to be added, but in my experience this has never been necessary. The PC expansion bus is not particularly fast, and most peripheral chips seem to be able to keep up with it. If you end up trying to add wait states, you are probably doing things the hard way, and might be better advised to have a complete rethink.

Some applications might require the added complication of using interrupts, but there are probably few PC add-ons where the use of interrupts is essential. This is a subject that is more a matter of software than hardware, and so it will not be pursued further here. Interrupts on

Fig.2.23 The 8255 and ADC0844 chips are available in plastic DIL encapsulations

the PC are less fraught than on most eight-bit computers, but you still need to be fairly expert at the software side of things. You have to get things just right or each time the add-on is activated it will crash the computer. Probably the best advice when designing PC add-ons is to use sensible choices for the chips that actually interface to the expansion bus. There are plenty of integrated circuits that will easily interface with the PCs which, which means that there is probably no point in using any devices that prove to be awkward.

Points to remember

The first stage in designing an ISA expansion card is to come up with a suitable address decoder circuit. The address decoder actually decodes a few control lines in addition to the lower 10 address lines.

The IOR line goes low during read cycles and the IOW line goes low during write cycles. This permits input and output ports to share the same address.

An ultra simple address decoder can decode as few as five address lines and two control lines. However, this places the device at every address in a block of 32 addresses. Decoding more address lines enables the 32 addresses to be used more efficiently, with a different device at each address if all 10 of the lower address lines are decoded.

An address decoder can be produced entirely from gates and inverters, but in many cases it is better to base the circuit on a more complex chip such as the 74LS138. This usually produces a more straightforward but versatile design.

Some interface chips are designed specifically for use with an 8080 style control bus. When using devices of this type it is not necessary to decode some of the control lines, since the chips have inputs for these lines. If a chip has more than one register, it will also decode one or more of the address lines.

It is generally better to resort to a special parallel input/output chip like the 8255 if a several parallel ports are required. Each 8255 chip can provide three eight-bit input/output ports that can be used in several modes.

The fact that a chip is described as something like "microprocessor compatible" does not necessarily mean that it is compatible with a microprocessor in the 8080 series. Using an interface chip designed for another type of processor might not be possible and is unlikely to be worth the effort.

With slow devices such as analogue to digital converters it is necessary to ensure that the device is not operated at an excessive rate, which would produce spurious data. Hardware handshaking is one solution, but in most cases a delay routine in the software is a simpler way of handling things.

Interfacing to the ISA bus is not a good starting point. Those with limited experience of electronics and interfacing should start with projects that interface to one of the external points such as the parallel port.

Printer port interfacing

Standard ports

While it has to be admitted that interfacing direct onto the PC expansion bus is in many ways the best approach, as we have seen in chapters one and two, it is also slightly awkward. It requires the use of custom printed circuit boards which must be accurately made (and of the double-sided variety), or projects based on proprietary prototyping cards. This second method is relatively straightforward, but it does not necessarily produce a very neat finished product, and the prototyping cards are not particularly cheap.

So is there a simpler way of connecting user add-ons to a PC? I suppose that this is a "how long is a piece of string?" style question. With some types of add-on circuit there is probably no realistic alternative to using the expansion slots. For example, if vast numbers of input/output lines are required, either a custom interface card must be produced, or your add-on must interface via a ready-made multi-line interface card. It is actually possible to have numerous input/output lines provided by other means, but this method of expansion is relatively cumbersome. With many of the more simple and straightforward projects though, the standard PC ports often offer a practical (and easier) alternative to the expansion bus.

Printer port

There are three types of standard PC port that are potentially usable for your own add-ons. These are the serial, parallel, and analogue ports. Interfacing via a serial port is not particularly difficult, and the serial-to-parallel and parallel-to-serial conversion is easily achieved using a UART (universal asynchronous receiver/transmitter). In most cases it is easier to use a parallel port, but for those who prefer the serial approach this topic is covered in the next chapter. Obviously most PCs have a printer port connected to a printer, and this port is therefore unavailable for general use unless you resort to some form "printer sharer" switching device. On the other hand, many PCs have a second printer port, and in most cases this is left totally unused. Even if a second port is not fitted, a very inexpensive expansion card is all that is needed in order to equip your computer with a second port. These days it is increasingly common for printers to have a USB port, and using this rather than the parallel interface frees the PC's printer port for other purposes.

Although a printer port may seem to be of limited use for general interfacing purposes, the PC printer ports are actually quite versatile. On the face of it a parallel printer port is an output type, and it has little or no potential for use as an input port. Fortunately, in addition to the eight data outputs a PC printer port has several handshake lines. In fact there are no less than nine of these - five inputs and four outputs. As we shall see later in this chapter, the handshake lines enable the port to act as an input or output type, or both at once. Some external circuitry is required in order to make the port function as an eight-bit input type, but it only requires a very simple and inexpensive add-on.

Obtaining eight inputs and eight output lines using one of the printer ports is certainly much easier than using a serial port or the expansion bus to provide the same function. Also, the parallel port can read and write at a much higher rate, and it still has some spare lines for general handshaking purposes or other uses. One possible use for these extra lines is to provide further eight-bit input or output ports. It is actually possible to obtain a large number of input and output lines using a printer port and basic multiplexing techniques. For complex interfacing of this type I would opt for a proper multi-port expansion card, but the printer port method is perfectly feasible if that is the approach you prefer.

Apart from PCs that date back many years, PCs have bidirectional printer ports. In other words, the eight data outputs can be switched to operate as inputs. Individual control over each line is not provided, so all eight lines have to be inputs or outputs. Even so, this greatly simplifies matters when an eight-bit input port and only a few outputs are required. It permits an eight-bit input to be provided without the need for additional hardware and software to "squeeze a quart into a pint pot".

Advantages

So why should you bother to use the PC's printer ports for general interfacing when there is a perfectly good expansion bus? As already pointed out, there are practical difficulties in using the expansion slots, making it a rather awkward prospect for the average electronics hobbyist. The printer and joystick ports are much more straightforward, and provide no real difficulties. You simply connect your add-on to the PC via a multi-way lead terminated in the appropriate type of D connector. Even if you are equipped to make accurate double-sided printed circuit boards, the relative simplicity of interfacing to the PC's built-in interfaces could reasonably be regarded as a more attractive proposition. It is noticeable that an increasing range of ready-made PC add-ons is designed to connect to the built-in interfaces rather than the expansion bus.

Another advantage of the built-in ports is that they effectively provide you with some of the hardware for your add-ons, but at little or no cost. At little cost if you need to buy an expansion card to provide the printer of "games" port, or no cost if your computer is supplied complete with suitable ports (as most are). If you interface via the expansion slots it is necessary to include address decoding and input/output ports on the card. This means that you end up with a fair amount of circuitry before you start on the project itself! Using the built-in ports means that all or most of the basic interfacing is taken care of for you.

On the face of it there is an advantage in using the expansion slots for your add-ons, as it keeps everything neat and tidy with your circuits tucked away inside the PC. In reality things are usually slightly less straightforward than this. You often seem to end up with projects that are half on the expansion card and half outside the computer, with a big lead between the two. This is because you often need to have access to the add-on. For example, EPROM programming and chip testing requires you to be able to plug chips into the add-on unit. If a project has any controls, these must be on an external unit so that you can get at them. With projects of these types, using the built-in ports would seem to be no more or less neat than using the expansion slots. It is likely to be significantly less expensive though.

Drawbacks

Using the integral ports does have one or two drawbacks. I suppose one of these drawbacks is that it is ultimately more limiting than using the expansion slots, but this is obviously irrelevant unless you intend to do some fairly complex interfacing. For many purposes the built-in ports are perfectly adequate. Another slight drawback is that there are no power rails available on the printer ports. Only a +5 volt rail is available when using the "games" port. When using the printer ports it is possible to use the "games" or keyboard port to provide a +5 volt supply, which is all that many add-ons require.

In the past, USB (universal serial bus) ports were relatively rare. They are actually present on the motherboards of many older PCs, but relatively few are equipped with connectors at the rear of the case to enable these ports to be connected to the outside world. These days they are present on the vast majority of PCs. Anyway, if your PC does have an unused USB port, this is another potential source of a +5 volt supply. When using the printer ports or game port it is possible to use the expansion bus as a source for all the PCs supply rails. However, this is not a particularly neat solution, and if anything beyond a simple +5 volt supply is needed, it is normal practice to provide the add-on with its own power supply unit.

Right lines

The PC printer connector is a female 25-way D type connector. You therefore need a male 25-way D connector to make the connections to each port. When used for their intended purpose the pins of each printer port have the functions detailed in Figure 3.1. This shows the port as viewed from the outside of the computer. Looking at it another way, it shows the pin functions of the male connector as viewed from rear. In other words, as viewed when you are actually making the connections to the plug.

If you are unsure about the pin numbering of practically any computer connector, it is worth bearing in mind that virtually all of these connectors have the pin numbers marked on the connectors themselves. Unfortunately, the small size of most connectors inevitably means that the lettering is very small. In the case of D type connectors, matters are not helped by the fact that the numbers are moulded into the plastic body of the connectors. You may well need the aid of a magnifier to read the numbers, but this is a certain method of avoiding a set of "mirrored" connections to the D plugs.

One way of using a printer port for general interfacing is to make your add-on circuit mimic a parallel printer, so that data can be written to it in the normal way. This method does have possible advantages, since there are operating system routines and general high level support to control the flow of data to the port. If you interface to the port in the normal way, there should be no difficulty in using these routines and support. The drawback of this method is that it is very restrictive, and

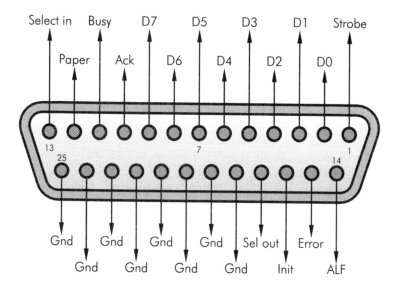

Fig.3.1 Connection details for a PC printer port

only permits the port to operate as a fairly basic eight-bit output type. This aspect of things is covered in more detail in the final chapter of this book.

Direct control of the printer ports permits much greater versatility, and in conjunction with some external hardware makes it possible to have numerous input and output lines. Even if you do wish to use the printer as nothing more than an eight-bit output with handshaking, it might still be easier to write direct to the port, and control the flow of data using your own software routines. This type of thing is not particularly complex, and is easily integrated with the main program. I would certainly recommend direct control of the ports wherever possible.

When taking direct control of the printer ports is best to largely forget the intended purposes of the input lines. The exception here are the eight data outputs ("D0" to "D7" in Figure 3.1). These are eight latching outputs, and it is to these that bytes of data a written when the ports are used to drive printers. Their function is normally the same when they are used for general interfacing purposes. The only difference when they are used for general interfacing is that you write data to the appropriate input/output address, and not to a DOS device via the operating system.

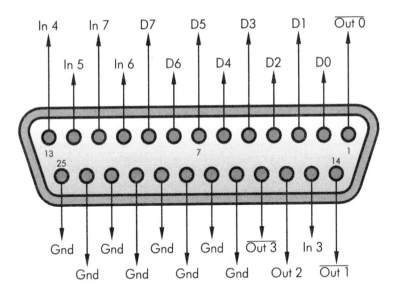

Fig.3.2 Connection details for a PC printer port when used as a general-purpose interface

With the other lines their original functions should be forgotten, and they should be thought of as input and output lines at certain addresses in the PC's input/output map. Figure 3.2 shows the pin functions with this alternative way of viewing things. As will be apparent from this diagram, in addition to the eight-bit output there are four other outputs, and five input lines. Unfortunately, some of these additional inputs and outputs have built-in inverters. These are the ones which have the line marked over the pin function. This is generally a bit inconvenient, but the inverters do not place any major limitations on the ways in which the relevant lines can be used. Where the inversions are not needed they can be counteracted by using external inverters in your interface circuit. Alternatively, the software routines can be written to take into account any unwanted inversions.

Properly addressed

In DOS terminology the printer ports are LPT1 and LPT2. They each occupy three addresses in the PC's input/output map. Note that the 8088 series of microprocessors used in the PCs have separate memory and input/output maps, and the printer ports are obviously in the input/

output map. When writing data to one of these ports, or reading from them, you must therefore use instructions that are appropriate to input/ output devices. Thus, in GW BASIC you would use INP and OUT, not PEEK and POKE. The normal scheme of things is for LPT1 to be at addresses from &H378 to &H37A, and LPT2 to be at addresses from &H278 to &H27A. The decimal equivalents for these hexadecimal address ranges are 888 to 890, and 632 to 634. In this book we will deal in hexadecimal addresses, but when writing software for use with your own printer port add-ons it is obviously in order to use decimal addresses if this is your preferred way of doing things.

This table shows the location of each printer port input/output line in the PC's input/output map.

I/O Line Address Mapping

LPT2

&H278

Bit	Line
0	D0
1	D1
2	D2
3	D3
4	D4
5	D5
6	D6
7	D7

&H279

Bit	Line
0	unused
1	unused
2	unused
3	In 3

4	In 4
5	In 5
6	In 6
7	In 7 (inverted)

&H27A

Bit	Line
0	Out 0 (inverted)
1	Out 1 (inverted)
2	Out 2
3	Out 3 (inverted)
4	unused
5	unused
6	unused
7	unused

LPT1

&H378

Bit	Line
0	D0
1	D1
2	D2
3	D3
4	D4
5	D5
6	D6
7	D7

&H379

Bit	Line
0	unused
1	unused
2	unused
3	In 3
4	In 4
5	In 5
6	In 6
7	In 7 (inverted)

&H37A

Bit	Line
0	Out 0 (inverted)
1	Out 1 (inverted)
2	Out 2
3	Out 3 (inverted)
4	unused
5	unused
6	unused
7	unused

There is a slight complication in that a third address block is sometimes used for PC printer ports. These addresses are &H3BC, &H3BD, and &H3BE. This address range seems to have its origins in the original Hercules graphics adapter, which included a parallel port. It is still used to some extent today, and many modern PCs can be set to use this address range via the BIOS Setup program. Apparently some PCs are supplied with this set as the address range for the built-in printer port. Where this address range is in use the operating system will use it for LPT1, with any ports at &H378 or &H278 being moved one port number higher as a result. Apparently, the operating system uses the port at the highest address as port 1, the one at the next highest address as port 2, and so on. Hence, where base address &H3BC is in use, it will always be used for printer port one. These are the locations of the input/output lines in the input/output map for a printer port having &H3BC as its base address:

LPT1 (base address &H3BC)

&H3BC

Bit	Line
0	D0
1	D1
2	D2
3	D3
4	D4
5	D5
6	D6
7	D7

&H3BD

Bit	Line
0	unused
1	unused
2	unused
3	In 3
4	In 4
5	In 5
6	In 6
7	In 7 (inverted)

&H3BE

Bit	Line
0	Out 0 (inverted)
1	Out 1 (inverted)

2	Out 2
3	Out 3 (inverted)
4	unused
5	unused
6	unused
7	unused

If you are controlling the ports directly, all this is not of any great significance, but you must obviously use the correct address range for the port in question. The BIOS will normally show a list of the base addresses for all the ports during the start-up routine, and this may tell you what you need to know. If not, you can always resort to trial and error to find the address range to which a port responds. Remember that in Windows you can use the System Information utility to provide a memory map for the input/output devices. This will show the address ranges for all the hardware, including all the standard ports.

Writing to the eight data lines of either port is very straightforward, and it is just a matter writing the correct value to the appropriate address. For example, to set all eight data lines of LPT2 high a value of 255 would be written to address &H278. In GW BASIC or Q BASIC this would achieved using the OUT instruction (i.e. OUT &H278,255). There is no need to include data latches in your add-on circuits, because the data outputs are latching types. The vast majority of modern PCs have bidirectional printer ports, but this complication can be ignored if you are using the data lines as outputs. They default to operation as normal outputs.

Handshake outputs

Like the data outputs, the four handshake outputs at addresses &H27A and &H37A are latching types, and they can only act as outputs. Again, it is just a matter of writing the appropriate value to the port address. With handshake lines it would usually be easier if they could be operated entirely independently. This is clearly not possible here, because all four handshake outputs of each printer port are at the same address. Therefore, when altering the state of one output, great care must be taken not to alter the states of the other three outputs.

A standard way of achieving this is to read from the port to determine the states of the outputs, and then work out a modified value to write back to the port, so that only the desired change is made. This is not a reliable method in this case, since this is a write-only address. You can not be sure that the values read back will accurately reflect the states of the outputs. In fact it is highly unlikely that they would, and with most printer port cards a value of 255 will always be returned from the handshake output address. This is simply because no hardware is actually activated by a read operation to the handshake output addresses, and the data lines of the microprocessor are left free to drift. They all drift to the high state, giving a returned value of 255. Where necessary, your software routines must therefore be carefully written so that the program "remembers" the last value written to the handshake outputs.

Of course, with only four of the bits at each of these addresses actually used, only data values from 0 to 15 are valid. Values from 16 to 255 will not cause a software error, but only the least significant four bits of these values will affect the states of the handshake outputs. For instance, a value of 16 would set all four outputs low, and a value of 255 would set them all high. On the other hand, it would not be good programming practice to write out-of-range values to a port.

Quart into a pint pot

One the face of it, the handshake inputs are only suitable for their intended purpose, since five inputs is not enough to read in bytes of data. In reality they can be used to read in bytes of data, but this requires a small amount of additional hardware, plus one of the handshake outputs. It is just a matter of using some basic multiplexing, and Figure 3.3 shows the basic set-up used. Four of the handshake inputs are fed from two sets of four-bit tristate buffers. The handshake output directly drives the enable input of one quad tristate buffer, but drives the enable input of the other via an inverter. Only one or other of the quad buffers will be active at any one time, and the required buffer can be selected by setting the handshake output to the appropriate state.

The lower nibble of the eight-bit input is applied to one buffer, and the upper nibble is applied to the other buffer. In order to read in a complete byte it is necessary to read the two nibbles separately and then use a simple software routine to combine the two readings in such a way that the correct value for the full byte is obtained. This method is obviously not as quick and direct as reading data in complete bytes, but even with a fairly slow PC it would probably be possible to read in a few hundred thousand bytes per second. It is certainly faster than using the serial ports, which enable data to be read at no more than a few kilobytes per second.

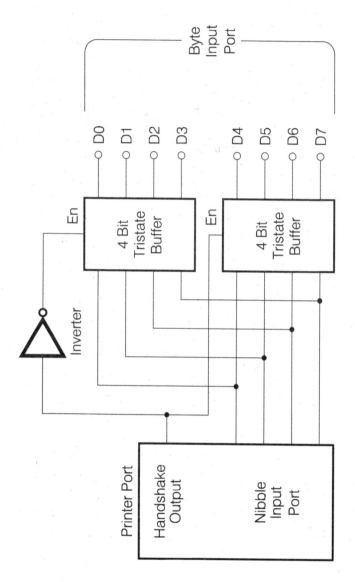

Fig.3.3 Using the printer port as an eight-bit input port

There is a potential problem though, and this is that the byte of data being read might change in the period between the first and second nibbles being read. This is problem that exists with any input method that provides something less than instant reading of a port. Where necessary, the problem must be dealt with using conventional handshake methods. For example, a handshake output could be used to latch input bytes into a data latch. The input port would then be used to read the bytes of data "frozen" in the data latch, rather than reading the bytes of data directly. Of course, in many cases the input data will change too slowly to create a major problem. However, even where the data changes relatively slowly it might be as well to use a software routine to check for inaccurate readings. For example, readings can be taken until three consecutive values are the same. This does not absolutely guarantee glitch-free results, but in practice would probably be sufficient to prevent any spurious readings.

Options

There is more than one way of interfacing this type of input port to the PC. Perhaps the obvious way is to drive the four most significant handshake lines from the quad buffers. The basic port reading process would then follow along these general lines. First the handshake output would be used to select the least significant nibble, and the port would be read. The returned value would then be placed into a variable. Next the handshake output would be used to select the most significant nibble, and a reading would be taken. This reading would then be stored in a second variable.

The value returned from the most significant nibble is correct, and needs no mathematical manipulation. The same is not true of the least significant nibble, which has been read in on the four most significant input lines. In order to make a correction for this it is merely necessary to divide the stored value by sixteen. Adding this value to the one read from the most significant nibble then gives the full value for the byte. In practice there is a slight problem with this method in that bit 7 is inverted. This is not a major problem as it can be corrected by using an inverter ahead of this input. Alternatively, further software could be used to invert this bit.

It is possible to avoid the problem of the inversion on bit seven by using bits three to six instead of bits four to seven. There are no internal inverters on bits three to six. The port reading process is much the same as before, with the most and least significant nibbles being read, and the returned values being placed into variables. The mathematical manipulation is obviously a bit different. This time the most significant nibble does require some correction, and this is achieved by simply multiplying it by two. A division by eight corrects the least significant nibble. Then, as before, the two values are added together to give the value for the complete byte.

It does not matter which of the four handshake outputs is used to control the quad tristate buffers. If there are two unused handshake outputs it is possible to dispense with the inverter. Instead, each buffer is controlled from a separate handshake output, and the software controls these in such a way that only one or other of the buffers is ever active at any one time. Of course, with this method a programming error could result in both buffers being active simultaneously, and some careful programming would be needed in order to avoid this. There is also a potential problem with both buffers being activated at switch-on, prior to your controlling software being run. This might not have disastrous results, but my preferred method is to include the inverter and use a single handshake output.

Using the method of interfacing outlined here it is possible for each printer port to provide an eight-bit latching output port, an eight-bit input port, plus two or three handshake outputs, and one handshake input. This is sufficient for many purposes, but it is actually possible to have further expansion per port if desired. In the same way that eight input lines can be multiplexed into four input lines, 16 input lines can be multiplexed into those eight lines. This is just a matter of using two eight-bit tristate buffers to provide the additional multiplexing, plus one of the spare handshake outputs to control the buffers.

Things could be taken a stage further, but multiplexing beyond 16 input lines produces a relatively complex circuit, and requires some convoluted programming in order to read the ports. My advice would be to use a proper parallel expansion card if large numbers of inputs are required. This is likely to be a more expensive way of tackling things, but it would also be a very much more straightforward and convenient solution to the problem.

Multiplexing techniques can also be applied to the eight data outputs, enabling two or more eight-bit output ports to be provided. Again, trying to provide numerous ports in this way is probably not very practical, and a proper parallel expansion card would then be a better option. Providing two or three ports in this way is reasonably straightforward though.

Input port

Having looked at the basic principles behind interfacing to the printer ports, we will now consider some practical circuits for input ports, and multiple input and output ports. We will start with basic eight-bit input ports. There are numerous ways of providing the required multiplexing, and the best method is largely dependent on the way in which the port will be used. In most cases it will not matter which method is used, and it is then just a matter of selecting the one that you find the most convenient. Here we will look at one solution that is suitable for most practical applications.

The circuit of Figure 3.4 is for an input port, which drives handshake, inputs from D3 to D6. This is the method I generally prefer, since it avoids to complication of the inversion on bit 7. There are various tristate buffers that can be used in this application, and in this circuit a 74LS244 octal tristate buffer is used. Although this chip is normally described as an octal buffer, it is in fact two four-bit types having separate enable inputs. This makes it ideal for use in the present application. IC2 provides an inversion so that the two halves of IC1 are driven in anti-phase.

Any of the four handshake outputs could be used to control the buffers, but to keep things as straightforward as possible the strobe output (bit 0 at pin 1 of the port) is used. The least significant nibble is read when pin 1 is low - the most significant nibble is read when pin 1 is high. However, bear in mind that there is a built-in inversion on the strobe output, so this output is set high and low using values of 0 and 1 respectively. This simple GW BASIC routine will read the port and print the returned value on the screen. This is for an interface on LPT1, but with the appropriate addresses it will also work with an interface on LPT2. The program should work using any BASIC that is compatible with GW BASIC, including Q BASIC.

```
5   REM PROG TO READ IN BYTE ON BITS 3 TO 6
10  OUT &H37A,1
20  LSN = INP(&H379) AND 120
30  LSN = LSN/8
40  OUT &H37A,0
50  MSN = INP(&H379) AND 120
60  MSN = MSN * 2
70  BYTE = LSN + MSN
80  PRINT BYTE
```

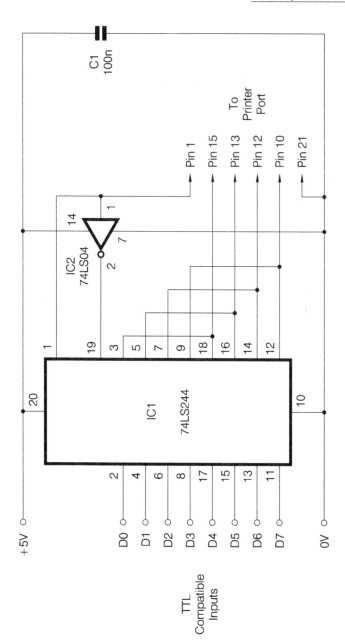

Fig.3.4 The circuit for a simple eight-bit input port

Line 10 sets the control output low so that the least significant nibble is selected. This nibble is then read at line 20 and placed in the variable called "LSN". The value read from the port is bitwise ANDed with a value of 120 so that only bits three to six are read, and the other four bits are masked. The bitwise ANDing process is described in detail in the chapter that deals with software matters. Those who are unfamiliar with this procedure would be well advised to study the relevant section of this book, since it is difficult to undertake anything more than some very basic computer interfacing without a proper understanding of bitwise ANDing.

The value held in LSN is incorrect, as the wrong lines (i.e. bits three to six instead of zero to three) have read it. When working in assembly language this type of thing can be handled using rotate or shift instructions to move the bits into the correct positions. When using a high level language it is easier to use multiplication or division to correct the positioning of bits. In this case a division by eight at line 30 produces the correct value for the least significant nibble. At line 40 the control output is set high so that the most significant nibble is selected. This nibble is then read at line 50, and the returned value is placed in a variable called "MSN". The value of this nibble is corrected at line 60 where it is multiplied by two. Finally, the values of the two nibbles are added together to produce the full eight-bit value, which is placed in the variable called "BYTE", and printed on the screen.

Although this single-chip solution to the tristate buffering looks very neat on paper, in reality it is something less than simplicity itself. The problem is simply that the pinout configuration of the 74LS244 is not as convenient as it might be. This is not a major problem if you have the necessary facilities to produce intricate printed circuit boards, but it makes life difficult if you are only able to produce relatively simple boards, or you wish to use a proprietary printed circuit board such as stripboard. For construction using stripboard, etc., the alternative circuit of Figure 3.5 should prove to be a better choice. This is based on two 74LS243 quad transceivers, but in this circuit both devices are connected to act as quad tristate buffers. The 74LS243 conveniently has all the inputs in one row of pins, and all the outputs in the other row. This makes it much easier to design a suitable component layout, particularly when using stripboard and other proprietary printed circuit boards.

The control input at pin 1 of each device is connected to the +5 volt rail, and the other control input at pin 13 of each chip then gives standard tristate control (high to enable the outputs, or low to disable them). As before, an inverter (IC2) is used to provide the required anti-phase control

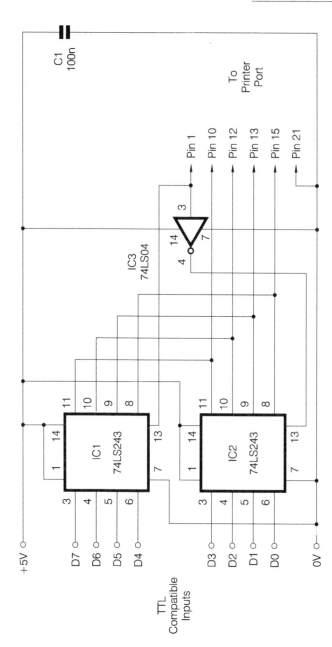

Fig.3.5 An alternative to the circuit of Fig.3.4

of the tristate buffers. Like the circuit of Figure 3.4, the control input must be low to read the least significant nibble, and high to read the most significant nibble. Therefore, the GW BASIC routine provided previously will also work with this version of the input port.

Dual inputs

It is not difficult to use the printer port's handshake lines to provide two eight-bit input ports, and it is just a matter of using additional multiplexing controlled by one of the spare handshake outputs. Figure 3.6 shows one way of providing the additional multiplexing. Note that this circuit requires an eight-bit input port, and that it must therefore be added onto one of the input ports described previously. It can not be used straight onto the printer port because the unaided printer port has an insufficient number of inputs. Of course, the situation is different if your PC has a bidirectional printer port, and doubling the number of inputs available from a bidirectional port is covered in the relevant section of this chapter.

The circuit is based on two 74LS541 eight-bit tristate buffers. Their inputs act as the two eight-bit input ports, and their outputs drive the basic eight-bit input port. IC3 is controlled direct from "Out 2" of the printer port (the "Initialise" handshake output), but IC2 is controlled via an inverter. If the basic input port uses one or two inverters, IC1 can be an unused section of the 74LS04 used in the basic input port circuit. The inversion provided by IC1 provides the required anti-phase operation of the buffers, with IC2 enabled when "Out 2" is high, and IC3 enabled when "Out 2" is low.

The 74LS541 actually has a two-input AND gate ahead of its active low enable input. The inputs of the gate are accessible at pins 1 and 19. The gating is not required in this case, so pin 19 is connected to the 0-volt rail, and pin 1 is used as a straightforward negative enable input. If it suits the component layout better, connect pin 1 to ground and use pin 19 as the control input. The circuit provides exactly the same action either way.

Obviously the way in which the dual port is read depends on the input port circuit utilised. For the sake of this example we will assume that it is connected to an input port of the type featured in Figure 3.4, 3.5, or an exact equivalent of these. If you use a different method of interfacing to the handshake inputs this routine will have to be amended accordingly. The routine on page 100 will read port 1 and print the returned value on the screen.

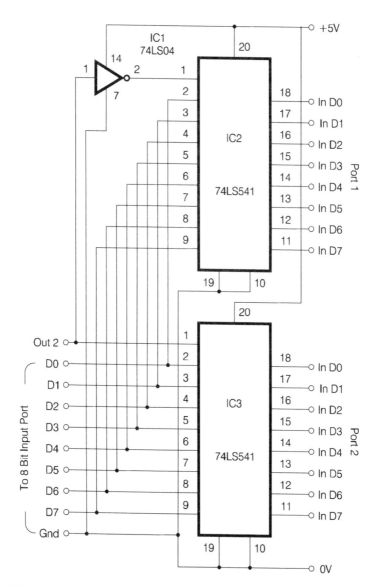

Fig.3.6 A simple method of providing two eight-bit input ports

```
5   REM PROG TO READ PORT 1
10  OUT &H37A,5
20  LSN = INP(&H379) AND 120
30  LSN = LSN/8
40  OUT &H37A,4
50  MSN = INP(&H379) AND 120
60  MSN = MSN * 2
70  BYTE = LSN + MSN
80  PRINT BYTE
```

This operates in exactly the same way as the program to read the basic input port, but lines 10 and 40 have been modified to take "Out 2" high, so that IC2 is activated and port 1 is selected. Remember that "Out 2", unlike the other three handshake outputs, does not have a built-in inversion. It is therefore set high using a value of 4, and low using a value of 0. This version of the program sets "Out 2" low so that port 2 is read.

```
5   REM PROG TO READ PORT 2
10  OUT &H37A,1
20  LSN = INP(&H379) AND 120
30  LSN = LSN/8
40  OUT &H37A,0
50  MSN = INP(&H379) AND 120
60  MSN = MSN * 2
70  BYTE = LSN + MSN
80  PRINT BYTE
```

Figure 3.7 shows the circuit for an alternative dual input circuit. This is based on two 74LS245 octal transceivers, which seem to be a bit easier to obtain than the 74LS541 tristate buffers. IC1 and IC2 are both hard wired into the "receive" mode by having pin 1 connected to ground. This effectively downgrades them to simple tristate buffers, controlled via the negative chip enable input at pin 19 of each device. Consequently, this circuit is functionally the same as that of Figure 3.6, and can be controlled using the same software routines.

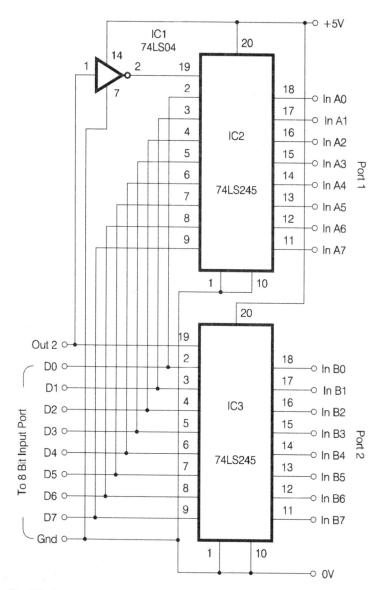

Fig.3.7 An alternative method of providing dual eight-bit input ports

Grabbing bytes

As pointed out previously, reading in bytes of data as two separate nibbles can cause problems when the data is changing fairly rapidly. A change between the first and second nibbles being read could produce completely erroneous results. This problem can be overcome by using an eight-bit data latch to "freeze" complete bytes which can then be read by one of the eight-bit input ports. This is the digital equivalent of an analogue sample-and-hold circuit. Data latching does not require much additional circuitry, but it does require an extra handshake output to control the data latch. Figure 3.8 shows one way of providing data latching.

IC1 is a 74LS373 octal "transparent" latch. When its control input at pin 11 is taken high, the binary pattern on the inputs is simply transferred straight through to the outputs. Taking pin 11 low "freezes" the outputs, and latches them with the data present on the inputs as pin 11 made the high-to-low transition. In this example pin 11 of IC1 is controlled by "Out 2", but it could be controlled by any spare handshake output. This GW BASIC program will latch data into IC1 and then read it. Again, for the sake of this example we will assume that the input port circuit of Figure 3.4 or 3.5 is being used.

```
10 REM PROG TO READ BYTE VIA DATA LATCH
(74LS373)
20 OUT &H37A,0
30 OUT &H37A,4
40 OUT &H37A,0
45 FOR DELAY = 1 TO 30000: NEXT DELAY
50 OUT &H37A,1
60 LSN = INP(&H379) AND 120
70 LSN = LSN/8
80 OUT &H37A,0
90 MSN = INP(&H379) AND 120
100 MSN = MSN * 2
110 BYTE = LSN + MSN
121'0 PRINT BYTE
```

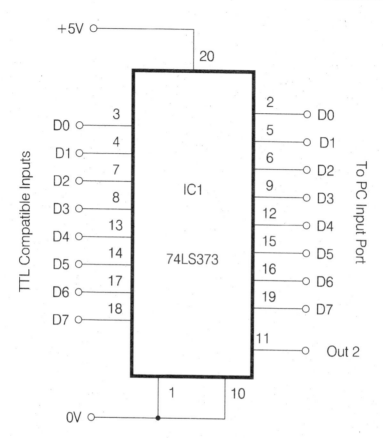

Fig.3.8 Using a 74LS373 as a data latch

This is just the normal port reading routine, but with lines 20 to 40 added to provide a positive latching pulse prior to the port being read. It is at line 40, where "Out 2" goes through a high-to-low transition, that the data is latched into the 74LS373. Line 45 is not part of the reading routine, and it simply provides a delay between the latching pulse and the latched data being read. This gives you an opportunity to alter the input data during this in-between period, so that the effectiveness of the latching can be checked. Obviously in normal use this line should be omitted.

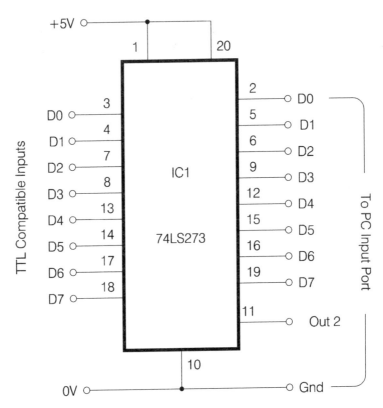

Fig.3.9 Using a 74LS273 as a data latch

Figure 3.9 shows an alternative data latch circuit. This is based on a 74LS273, which is an octal D type flip/flop. It works as a data latch if pin 11 is normally held high and is briefly pulsed low in order to latch a fresh byte of data. It is on the low-to-high transition that the data on the outputs is "frozen". Unlike the 74LS373, the 74LS273 is never "transparent". Data can only be transferred from the inputs to the outputs by using the latching process. Note also, that control of the 74LS273 is the opposite way round to the 74LS373, with a low pulse being used to latch the data. This circuit therefore needs slightly modified control software. The GW BASIC program on page 106 will latch data into the 74LS273 and then read it.

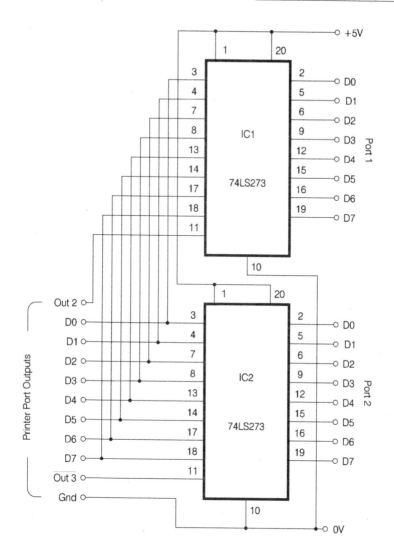

Fig.3.10 A circuit using two 74LS273 data latches that provides two eight-bit output ports

```
10 REM PROG TO READ BYTE VIA DATA LATCH
(74LS273)
20 OUT &H37A,4
30 OUT &H37A,0
40 OUT &H37A,4
45 FOR DELAY = 1 TO 30000: NEXT DELAY
50 OUT &H37A,1
60 LSN = INP(&H379) AND 120
70 LSN = LSN/8
80 OUT &H37A,0
90 MSN = INP(&H379) AND 120
100 MSN = MSN * 2
110 BYTE = LSN + MSN
121'0 PRINT BYTE
```

Dual Outputs

The eight data outputs of the printer port (D0 to D5 in Figures 3.1 and 3.2) provide a ready-made eight-bit output port. This makes writing bytes of data much easier than reading them, since it is possible to write complete bytes. Simply write the appropriate value to input/output address &H378 (LPT1) or &H278 (LPT2) and the data lines will take up the correct binary pattern. There are no inversions on any of these lines, and they are all TTL compatible.

Using the single eight-bit output to provide two eight-bit outputs is very simple, and it requires nothing more than a couple of data latches, with each one controlled from a separate handshake output. Figure 3.10 shows one way of providing an extra output port. This uses two 74LS273 octal D type flip/flops as the data latches. The handshake control lines are normally held in the high state. In order to write a byte of data to port 1 the data is first written to the data lines of the printer port. The handshake line used to control IC1 ("Out 2" in this example) is then taken low and high again. On the low-to-high transition the new byte of data is latched onto IC1's outputs. Data is written to port 2 in much the same way, but it is handshake line "Out 3" that is pulsed low in order to latch the new byte of data onto the outputs of port 2.

The negative reset inputs of IC1 and IC2 are simply connected to the positive supply rail so that they have no effect. If preferred, a C - R network can be used to provide a negative pulse at switch-on to ensure that all the outputs of both ports start out in the low state. This is only necessary where random values on the port outputs could have dire consequences. It might require a very long reset pulse to ensure that the computer's start-up and initial testing routines do not override the reset pulse.

The software to write data to the ports is very simple. This example in GW BASIC will write a value of 123 to port 1.

```
10 REM PROG TO WRITE A BYTE OF DATA TO PORT 1
(74LS273 LATCHES)
20 OUT &H37A,4
30 OUT &H378,123
40 OUT &H37A,0
50 OUT &H378,4
```

Line 20 sets the handshake outputs at their correct initial states, which is with both of them in the high state. Remember that "Out 3" has a built-in inversion, and a value of zero rather than eight is therefore needed in order to set this line high. The data is written to the printer port's data lines at line 30, and then the next two lines produce a low pulse on "Out 2", while leaving "Out 3" high. It is on the low-to-high transition produced by line 50 that the fresh byte of data appears on the outputs of port 1.

Writing data to port 2 uses a similar process. This example GW BASIC routine writes a value of 231 to port 2.

```
10 REM PROG TO WRITE A BYTE OF DATA TO PORT 2
(74LS273 LATCHES)
20 OUT &H37A,4
30 OUT &H378,231
40 OUT &H37A,12
50 OUT &H37A,4
```

Again, line 20 sets the correct initial states on the handshake outputs, and the value for port 2 is written to the printer port data lines at line 30. Lines 40 and 50 then provide a negative pulse on "Out 3", but leave "Out 2" high so that the data on the port 1 outputs is left unchanged. Of course, if it was necessary to write the same byte of data to both ports, this could be achieved by writing the data to the printer port data lines, and then pulsing both "Out 2" and "Out 3".

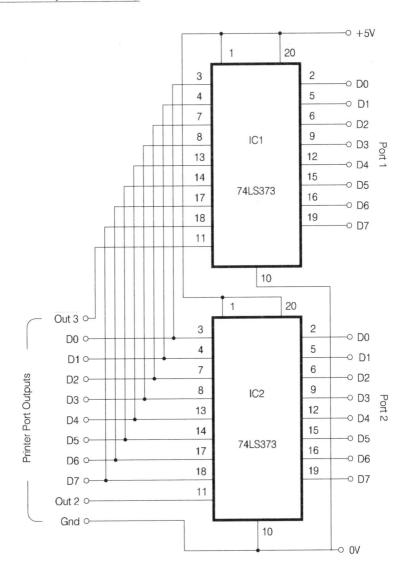

*Fig.3.11 An alternative method of providing two eight-bit output ports.
This circuit uses two 74LS373 data latches*

Figure 3.11 shows an alternative method of providing twin eight-bit output ports. This operates in much the same way as the circuit of Figure 3.10, but in this case the data latches are 74LS373 octal transparent latches. The only significant difference when using this method is that the handshake outputs should normally be low, and pulsed high in order latch data into their respective latches. This GW BASIC routine will write a value of 156 to port 1.

```
10 REM PROG TO WRITE A BYTE OF DATA TO PORT 1
(74LS373 LATCHES)
20 OUT &H37A,8
30 OUT &H378,156
40 OUT &H37A,0
50 OUT &H37A,8
```

This GW BASIC program will write a value of 54 to port 2.

```
10 REM PROG TO WRITE A BYTE OF DATA TO PORT 2
(74LS373 LATCHES)
20 OUT &H37A,8
30 OUT &H378,156
40 OUT &H37A,4
50 OUT &H37A,8
```

Of course, with four handshake outputs available on the printer port it is possible to extend this basic scheme of things to provide three or four eight-bit output ports. The only problem is that this tends to tie up the handshake outputs so that there is little scope for providing extra input lines, or for using the handshake outputs for their intended purpose. In practice it might therefore be better to opt for a proper parallel interface card if a large number of outputs are required. It is perfectly possible to provide up to 32 output lines though.

Bidirectional operation

Most modern PC printer ports, whether built-in or provided via expansion cards, are bidirectional. In other words, the eight data lines can set to operate as inputs. It is not possible to have split operation with some

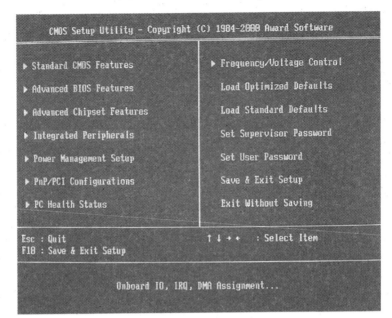

Fig.3.12 The initial screen of an Award BIOS Setup program

lines as inputs and others as outputs. The port can only operate in the normal output mode, or with all the lines as inputs. Even so, this provides much greater versatility, and makes life much easier if you only require an eight-bit input port plus some handshake lines. There is no need to use any external hardware to achieve this; you simply set the data lines to act as inputs and make use of whichever of the nine handshake lines you require.

It also makes the software side of things much easier, since bytes of data can be read in a single instruction. It is only fair to point out that in some circumstances it might be better to use the handshake inputs to read in bytes of data, rather than using the data lines. If you require eight-bit input and output ports, using the handshake inputs and some hardware to provide the inputs, and the data lines to act as the outputs almost certainly represents the easiest way of doing things.

How do you determine whether or not your parallel printer ports are capable of bidirectional operation? You can simply adopt the "suck it and see" approach, but this is not as reliable as you might expect, because not all printer ports default to bidirectional operation. Also,

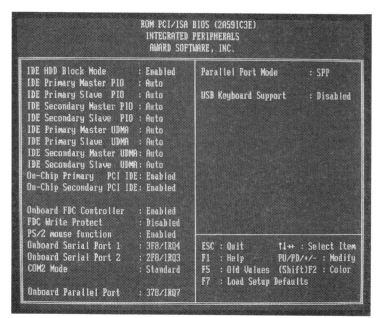

Fig.3.13 The Integrated Peripherals section

there is more than one bidirectional mode, and the port could simply be set to the wrong one. If you are using a port provided by an expansion card you should look carefully at the instruction manual or leaflet supplied with the card. If more than one mode of operation is supported this should make it clear how each one is obtained. This will normally mean setting jumpers or DIP switches to select the required mode. There may be something like a "normal" mode, which only provides data outputs, and an SPP or EPP mode. These are the "standard parallel port" and "enhanced parallel port" modes, either of which will provide the basic two-way operation that we require.

Motherboards usually have the parallel port controlled via the BIOS Setup program. With most PCs the BIOS Setup program is entered by pressing the "Del" key at the appropriate point is the initial boot-up routine. However, there are plenty of alternative methods such as pressing the Esc or Ins key. Usually there is an onscreen message during the initial testing routine that indicates which key or keys to operate. If in doubt you should consult the instruction manual for your computer or the manual for its motherboard.

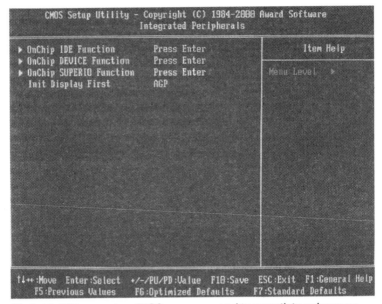

Fig.3.14 With a modern BIOS you may need to negotiate submenus

Modern Setup programs are quite large, and have the available options in half a dozen or so groups. Figure 3.12 shows the initial screen produced by an Award BIOS, and it is really an outsize menu. Use the cursor key to highlight the required option and then operate the Return key to enter that menu. The serial and parallel port settings are usually in a section called something like "Integrated Peripherals". Figure 3.13 shows this section of an Award BIOS. The address and IRQ (interrupt request) number for the port are set via the entry at the bottom of the left-hand section.

The parallel port's mode is set via the entry at the top of the right-hand section of the screen. In this case the cursor keys are used to select the required parameter, and the Pg Up and Pg Dn keys on the numeric keypad are then used to alter the setting. However, the exact method of control varies from one BIOS manufacturer to another. There are usually onscreen prompts that indicate the functions of the important keys.

The size of a modern BIOS Setup program is such that it might be necessary to go into a submenu in order to find the section that deals with the parallel port. In the example of Figure 3.14 there are three

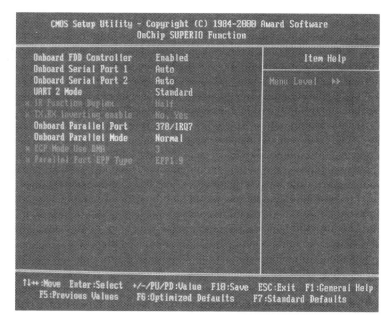

Fig.3.15 The settings for the parallel port are in the SUPERIO section of this BIOS

submenus to choose from, and it is not immediately obvious which one gives access to the parallel port's parameters. The manual for the computer or its motherboard might provide some help, but if necessary you will have to do some exploring. With this version of the Award BIOS I found the parallel port's settings in the SUPERIO section (Figure 3.15).

Any EPP or SPP mode should be suitable for basic bidirectional use. With an old BIOS the Standard mode is an output only mode, where the port functions as a basic printer port with no input facility on the data lines. With a modern BIOS the Standard setting is the SPP mode, and there is no output only mode. This is acceptable, because the SPP mode is fully compatible with software written for a straightforward printer port. As pointed out previously, an SPP port defaults to the output mode. With the more recent motherboards there is also likely to be an ECP (extended capabilities parallel port) mode, and although this provides a form or bidirectional operation, it does not seem to provide the basic method of control we require.

Direction control

As we have already seen, when set for bidirectional operation a printer port defaults to the output mode, and operates in exactly the same manner as an ordinary printer port. This gives compatibility with software written for ports that do not support bipolar operation, but it does produce a slight problem. It is something that must be borne in mind when using the port as an input type, because it means that initially the outputs of your project will be driving the outputs of the printer port. This could lead to large currents flowing, and possible damage to the printer port or your project.

Most bidirectional printer ports have current limiting on the data outputs to ensure that no damage occurs, but it is advisable to take no chances and include current limiting resistors between the outputs of your project and the printer port data lines. The values of these resistors must be high enough to ensure that only safe currents can flow, but low enough to permit the circuits to function correctly. A value of around 220R to 270R is satisfactory.

Setting the port to the input mode is easy enough, and is achieved via bit five at the handshake output address (normally &H37A for LPT1, and &H27A for LPT2). The four least significant bits of this address are used to control the handshake outputs of the port, and due care must be taken not to alter the settings of the handshake lines when setting the port to the input mode. Similarly, you must make sure that the port is not inadvertently set back to the output mode when writing data to the handshake lines.

This basically just boils down to always writing 32 (decimal) more than normal to the handshake output register so that bit five is always at logic one. Also, make sure that the handshake lines are set to the appropriate starting levels and bit five is set high before the first read operation on the data lines. If the handshake outputs are not in use, simply write a value of 32 to the handshake output register at the start of the program and ignore this register thereafter.

A simple GW BASIC or QBASIC program is all that is needed in order to check whether or not a printer port is operating properly in the input mode. This program tests a port that has its base address at &H378, but it will obviously work with other ports if the two appropriate addresses are used.

```
10 REM BIDIRECTIONAL PORT TEST PROGRAM
20 CLS
30 OUT &H37A,32
40 LOCATE 10,30
50 PRINT INP(&H378)
60 GOTO 20
```

Line 20 clears the screen and line 30 sets the port to the input mode. Lines 40 and 50 then position the cursor towards the middle of the screen and print the value returned from the port. This routine is then repeated indefinitely, with a rapidly updated value being displayed on the screen. With most printer ports this will result in "255" being displayed on the screen, due to the use of pull-up resistors on the inputs. With other ports the inputs seem to have a high input impedance, and will be left "floating". If "255" is displayed, connecting one or two inputs to the 0-volt rail via current limiting resistors of about 330R in value should produce a reduced reading (e.g. 254 if D0 is pulled low). If the inputs are high impedance types, simply placing a finger close to the data terminals of the port will probably be sufficient to produce changes in the reading.

If no change in the reading can be produced, either the port is not a bidirectional type or it has not been set to a suitable mode. There are actually a few PCs that have built-in printer ports that support bidirectional operation, but which do not handle things in the standard manner. With a port of this type it should be possible to use it in the input mode if you can obtain the manufacturer's technical information on the PC's hardware, but using an add-on printer port card might be a better solution. Fortunately, these days the vast majority of PCs use the method of direction control described here.

The multiplexing technique described previously can be used to increase the number of input lines available, and the circuits of Figure 3.6 and 3.7 will work well with a bidirectional printer port. However, remember to include the current limiting resistors between all the tristate buffers and the input port.

Laptop port

It is perhaps worth mentioning that the printer ports of laptop computers can be problematic with home constructed add-ons. Support for bidirectional operation seems to be less than universal, although most modern laptop computers support it. The main problem seems to be due to laptop computers generally operating at something less than normal 5-volt logic levels. Their main circuits usually operate at about 3 volts or so, and in many cases a higher voltage is not used for the printer port. These ports exploit the fact that something less than 5-volts constitutes a valid logic 1 level. Trouble-free results are normally obtained using interface chips that operate at TTL logic levels, where a minimum of about 2.7 volts is sufficient to represent a logic 1 level. Devices that operate at other than TTL logic levels can give problems.

This difficulty can usually be overcome by using 74HCT series buffers on the port's outputs. These buffers should operate reliably from a port operating at a lower than normal supply voltage, and will drive most interface chips reliably. Of course, the buffers must be run from a normal 5-volt supply and must not be run from the lower supply potential of the laptop computer. Driving the port's inputs is usually less troublesome, but I suppose there could be problems with the logic 0 voltage being too high, causing it to be interpreted as logic 1 by the port. Driving the inputs via 74HC series buffers should cure this problem. The outputs of this logic family operate at normal CMOS voltages, which means that the logic 0 output level will be little more than 0-volts.

Serial approach

A serial approach to interfacing projects to a parallel port might sound like a contradiction in terms, but it does have advantages. It would probably be more accurate to say that it does have its advantage. The obvious point in favour of serial interfacing is that two or three lines can be used to handle eight bits of data. In fact, there is theoretically no limit to the number of bits that can be handled by a serial link, so it is perfectly possible to have something like two lines providing three or four eight-bit output ports. A serial link can operate in either direction, so something like two or three lines providing three eight-bit input ports is also possible. There is another potential advantage, which is the ability of serial interfaces to operate over longer distances than parallel alternatives. However, the greater operating range is not needed in most practical applications, and the longer operating range can be difficult to achieve in practice.

Of course, the serial approach has its drawbacks as well. The obvious one is that the maximum rate at which data can be transferred is much lower. The larger the number of bits the link has to handle, the lower the rate at which complete bytes, words, etc., can be transferred. There are many applications where speed is not of any importance, and serial interfacing is well suited to these. For example, an interface that is

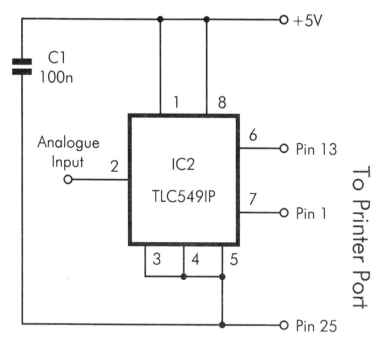

Fig.3.16 The circuit diagram for the serial ADC

monitoring two temperature sensors will probably need to update its readings only once every few seconds, or even once every few minutes, because changes in temperature will only occur very slowly. Something like audio digitising is less well suited to serial interfacing, although even in this application it would probably be possible using suitable fast software and hardware.

Serial ADC

No doubt it would be easy enough to use shift registers such as the 74HC164 and 74HC166 to provide the basis of a synchronous serial link, but there are plenty of chips that are specifically designed for this method of interfacing. These devices can interface direct to a PC's parallel port via typically three or four lines. The TLC549IP analogue-to-digital converter is used here as an example of reading data via a synchronous serial interface. However, other serial interface chips operate using the

117

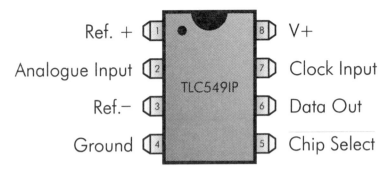

Fig.3.17 Pin functions for the TLC549IP, etc.

same basic principles. Analogue converters are well suited to serial interfacing as they mostly operate at relatively slow speeds, and the slowness of the link to the PC is unlikely to be of any consequence.

The circuit diagram for the converter is shown in Figure 3.16, and Figure 3.17 shows the pin functions for the TLC549IP converter chip. Although a TLC549IP is specified for IC1, the circuit will work just as well using other chips from this series, such as the TLC548IP and TLC548CP. The circuit is not exactly over-engineered, with just two components. The only discrete component needed is supply decoupling capacitor C1. There are separate inputs for the positive and negative reference voltages, but in most applications the Ref.- input is simply connected to ground. The full-scale value is then equal to the voltage applied to the Ref.+ input. In this example the 5-volt supply is used as the reference voltage, but a highly stable voltage reference can be used instead. Note that the reference potential should not be less than 2.5 volts.

The TLC549IP contains an eight-bit successive approximation converter that has its own clock generator. In order to simplify interfacing there is no start conversion input. Instead, a new conversion is automatically commenced at the end of the eighth clock cycle when the previous sample has been fully clocked out. One slight drawback of this system is that the first byte of data obtain from the device is not the result of a reading, and is simply "noise". The first byte must therefore be discarded.

The chip includes a sample and hold circuit, which avoids erroneous results with rapidly changing input voltages. This is operated automatically when the conversion is started. It takes a maximum of 36 system clock cycles for the conversion to be completed. The typical conversion time is eight microseconds for the TLC548IP and TLC548CP,

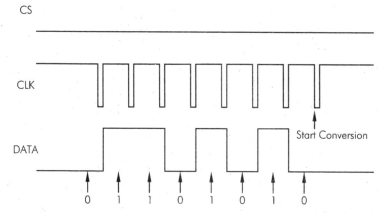

Fig.3.18 Timing diagram for the TLC548/9 series of chips

and 12 microseconds for the TLC549IP. However, the maximum conversion time for all three chips is 17 microseconds.

There is no status output to indicate that the conversion has been completed, so where necessary a timing loop must be used in the software to prevent the converter from being read prematurely. Even with a fast PC, a timing loop might not be necessary with some programming languages. Where a high conversion rate is needed you can adopt a "suck it and see" approach, with a delay only being added if the readings from the converter seem to be erratic. If a high conversion rate is not required, it makes sense to add a delay to ensure that a generous amount of time is allowed for each conversion.

Synchronous data

Once a conversion has been completed, data is clocked out of the chip using standard synchronous methods. The first bit of data is placed on the data output at pin 6, and this is read by the computer. A pulse is then applied to the clock input at pin 7 in order to move the next bit of data out onto pin 6. This is read by the computer, another clock pulse is supplied to pin 7, and so on until all eight bits of data have been read. Another clock pulse is then used to start the next conversion. A software routine in the PC is used to reassemble the individual bits of data back into a complete byte. Once the data has been read, the chip select input is then returned to the high state. The circuit is then ready to commence another conversion.

The timing diagram of Figure 3.18 shows a typical read cycle. In this application the tristate capability of the Data Output is not required, since it is not being interfaced to the microprocessor's data bus. The Chip Select (CS) input is therefore connected to ground so that the Data Output is permanently enabled. The first bit of data can be read from the chip once the conversion has been completed. A clock pulse is then generated, the next bit is read, another clock pulse is generated, the next bit is read, and so on until all eight bits have been read. The arrows show the approximate places that the data is read from the data line. Finally, another clock pulse is generated and a new conversion is commenced.

The clock signal is shown as a regular train of pulses in Figure 3.18, but the synchronous approach does not require this sort of strict timing. Provided the data output is read at the appropriate times between the clock pulses and the clock rate is not too high, the exact timing of the clock signal is unimportant. The software has to ensure that things happen in the right order, rather than at precise moments in time.

The method of interfacing used in Figure 3.16 is to have the Clock Input driven from the Strobe output (Out 0), and the data read via the Select input (In 4). However, it should be possible to interface this circuit to any two output lines and any input line. It is best to use the printer port's handshake lines to interface to serial devices, leaving the eight data lines free to act as a parallel input or output port. Since the analogue to digital converter uses only three of the port's nine handshake lines there are still six left for use as handshake lines (two outputs and four inputs). Alternatively, they can be used to interface another serial chip.

Software

The synchronous serial approach to interfacing simplifies the hardware, but it certainly makes the software much more complex. It usually takes no more than half a dozen lines of code to read a parallel analogue to digital converter, but much longer routines are needed to accommodate serial chips. This GW BASIC/QBASIC program reads the converter and prints the returned values at a fixed point on the screen:

Listing 1

```
10 REM A/D converter program (TLC548/9)
20 CLS
30 FOR L = 1 TO 7
40 OUT &H37A,1
50 OUT &H37A,0
60 NEXT L
70 OUT &H37A,1
80 OUT &H37A,0
90 X = INP(&H379) AND 16
100 X = X*8
110 OUT &H37A,1
120 OUT &H37A,0
130 Y = INP(&H379) AND 16
140 Y = Y*4
150 X = X + Y
160 OUT &H37A,1
170 OUT &H37A,0
180 Y = INP(&H379) AND 16
190 Y = Y * 2
200 X = X + Y
210 OUT &H37A,1
220 OUT &H37A,0
230 Y = INP(&H379) AND 16
240 X = X + Y
250 OUT &H37A,1
260 OUT &H37A,0
270 Y = INP(&H379) AND 16
280 Y = Y/2
290 X = X + Y
300 OUT &H37A,1
310 OUT &H37A,0
320 Y = INP(&H379) AND 16
330 Y = Y/4
340 X = X + Y
350 OUT &H37A,1
360 OUT &H37A,0
```

```
370 Y = INP(&H379) AND 16
380 Y = Y/8
390 X = X + Y
400 OUT &H37A,1
410 OUT &H37A,0
420 Y = INP(&H379) AND 16
430 Y = Y/16
440 Z = X + Y
450 LOCATE 10,10
460 PRINT "          "
470 LOCATE 10,10
480 PRINT Z
490 OUT &H37A,1
500 GOTO 70
```

Line 20 clears the screen and then the next four lines generate a series of seven clock pulses, with an eighth pulse being produced by lines 70 and 80. The series of seven pulses is generated using a pair of OUT instructions within a FOR...NEXT loop. The purpose of the eight pulses is to start the first conversion, which is triggered by the eighth pulse. The data clocked out from the converter chip is garbage and is discarded. Bear in mind that the Strobe output line is inverted, so writing 1 to &H37A sets this output low, and writing 0 to this address sets the Strobe output high. The OUT instructions therefore repeatedly set the Strobe line low and then high. Note that the addresses used in this program are for what will usually be printer port 1 (LPT1). Where appropriate, the addresses must be changed to suit the particular port you are using.

On the face of it, a delay is needed after line 80 to prevent premature reading of the converter. In practice it is by no means certain that the program will run fast enough to require a delay. It only takes a matter of microseconds to complete each conversion, and interpreted languages such as GW BASIC and QBASIC are not particularly fast. I did not find a delay necessary when running the program in GW BASIC using a 1.333-gigahertz Athlon computer. Using assembly language or a compiled language, the added speed would probably necessitate the inclusion of a delaying routine.

The first bit of data is read at line 90, using a bitwise AND operation to mask all but the correct bit. The returned value is 16 if the Data Output of the converter chip is high, or zero if it is low. The first bit of data is the most significant bit, which should give a value of 128 or zero rather than

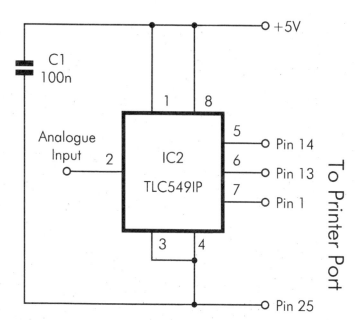

Fig.3.19 The improved serial ADC circuit

16 or zero. Therefore, the returned value is multiplied by 8. Another clock pulse is then generated, and the Data Output is read again. This time bit 6 is being read, and the returned value should be 0 or 64. The returned value is therefore multiplied by four in order to give the correct figure. This value is then added to the previous reading and stored in variable X. This process continues until all eight bits have been read. Where necessary, the returned value is corrected before being added to variable X. The final value stored in Z is the full eight-bit reading from the converter.

The last few lines of the program position the cursor on the screen, print spaces on the screen to blank any previous reading, reposition the cursor, and then print the new reading on the screen. At line 500 the program is looped back to line 70 where a clock pulse is produced. This starts another conversion, which is then read and printed on the screen. The program takes and prints readings on the screen indefinitely. The usual Control-Break key combination can be used to exit the program.

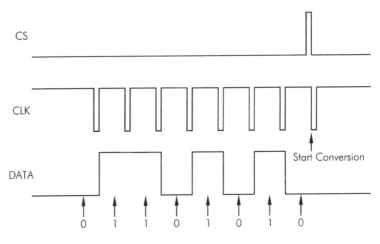

Fig.3.20 Timing diagram for the inproved serial ADC

Out of sync

Simple two-wire synchronous links of the type used with this analogue-to-digital converter are little used in practice. It works well enough provided there are no glitches somewhere along the line. In the real world it is quite likely that glitches or a lack of continuity will cause the system to go wrong. If you try this analogue-to-digital converter it will almost certainly work properly and continue to do so for thousands of readings. However, problems are likely to occur if you try stopping the program and then restarting it.

The root of the problem is that the program will stop at a random line number, not at the end of one complete read cycle. The clock signal is therefore likely to stop with some of the last conversion clocked out, and some still in the chip. The program "thinks" it is starting from scratch when it is restarted, but there is actually some data left in the chip. It clocks out a few bits of data from the previous reading, starts a new conversion, and then clocks out a few more bits. Each reading contains part of the previous conversion and part of the new one, with the bits all shifted out of position. The returned values are therefore erroneous.

The normal way around this problem is to have a third connecting wire that permits the computer to set the serial chip to a definite starting state.

This additional line is often used to operate a reset input on the serial chip. In the case of an analogue to digital converter there is often a Start Conversion input. In either case the controlling software can initialise the serial chip before reading or sending a data stream. This should avoid things getting out of synchronisation in the first place, and will almost immediately recover the situation if an error should occur.

The TLC548/9 chips do not have a reset input as such, but the Chip Select input can be used to prevent the chip and the controlling software from getting out of synchronisation. The converter circuit can therefore be made more reliable by driving the Chip Select input of the TLC548/9 from an output of the printer port. Figure 3.19 shows the revised circuit for the analogue-to-digital converter. Instead of the Chip Select input being tied to ground it is driven from the Error output (Out 1) at pin 15. In order to keep readings properly synchronised it is merely necessary to pulse the Chip Select input high before the eighth clock pulse is produced (Figure 3.20). This ensures that a new conversion is started on the next clock pulse, effectively forcing it to become the eighth clock pulse. If the pulse is actually (say) the fourth pulse, the current byte of data will be garbage, but things will be back in synchronisation for the next byte.

This is the modified version of the program. It is just a matter of adding an extra OUT instruction after the FOR...NEXT loop, so that the required pulse is produced on the Chip Select input.

Listing 2

```
10 REM Synched A/D converter program (TLC548/9)
20 CLS
22 FOR L = 1 TO 7
24 OUT &H37A,3
26 OUT &H37A,2
28 NEXT L
30 OUT &H37A,1
40 OUT &H37A,3
50 OUT &H37A,2
60 X = INP(&H379) AND 16
70 X = X*8
80 OUT &H37A,3
90 OUT &H37A,2
100 Y = INP(&H379) AND 16
110 Y = Y*4
```

```
120 X = X + Y
130 OUT &H37A,3
140 OUT &H37A,2
150 Y = INP(&H379) AND 16
160 Y = Y * 2
170 X = X + Y
180 OUT &H37A,3
190 OUT &H37A,2
200 Y = INP(&H379) AND 16
210 X = X + Y
220 OUT &H37A,3
230 OUT &H37A,2
240 Y = INP(&H379) AND 16
250 Y = Y/2
260 X = X + Y
270 OUT &H37A,3
280 OUT &H37A,2
290 Y = INP(&H379) AND 16
300 Y = Y/4
310 X = X + Y
320 OUT &H37A,3
330 OUT &H37A,2
340 Y = INP(&H379) AND 16
350 Y = Y/8
360 X = X + Y
370 OUT &H37A,3
380 OUT &H37A,2
390 Y = INP(&H379) AND 16
400 Y = Y/16
410 Z = X + Y
420 OUT &H37A,3
430 LOCATE 10,10
440 PRINT "          "
450 LOCATE 10,10
460 PRINT Z
470 OUT &H37A,1
480 GOTO 40
```

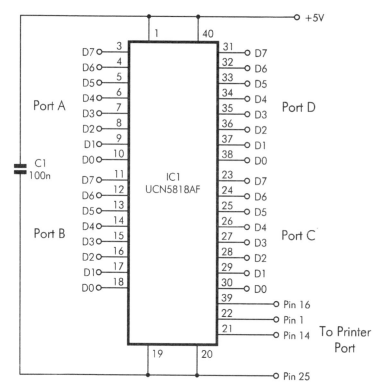

Fig.3.21 The circuit diagram for the 32-bit output port

Clocking out

In the analogue-to-digital converter example, serial data is read from the interface chip. Synchronous serial links operate just as well in the opposite direction though, with about three lines being used to supply bytes or words to the interface chip. Figure 3.21 shows the circuit diagram for a simple serial interface that provides not less than four eight-bit output ports. Like the analogue-to-digital converter, it requires just one chip and a supply decoupling capacitor. The outputs are shown in Figure 3.21 as four eight-bit output ports, but the 32 output lines can be organised in any desired fashion, such as twin 18-bit ports.

The UCN5818AF used for IC1 is primarily designed for use with relatively high voltage loads, but this ability is not needed in most interfacing

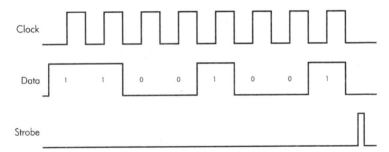

Fig.3.22 The timing diagram for the 32-bit output port. In this example only eight bits are output

applications. Consequently, both of its supply pins are connected to a normal +5-volt logic supply. The Blanking input at pin 19 can switch off all 32 outputs, effectively setting them at logic 0, but this facility is not needed in most applications. Pin 19 is therefore connected to ground so that the outputs are permanently enabled.

In the unlikely even that 32 outputs is insufficient, pin 2 provides a clock output that permits two devices to be connected in series, giving 64 outputs. Connect pin 2 of the first chip to the Data Input (pin 39) of the second chip, and drive the two clock inputs (pin 21 of each chip) in parallel. In theory, a large number of chips could be connected in series, giving hundreds of outputs. In practice such an interface would probably be so slow and cumbersome as to be of little value, so it is probably best to use no more than two or three of these chips in series.

Clocking data into the chip is very straightforward, and the timing diagram of Figure 3.22 shows the method used. This diagram has been simplified to show a single byte of data being sent to the chip, and in practice groups of 32 clock cycles and bits of data would be used. The basic principle is the same though. The appropriate logic level for the first bit is set on the Data Input, and a clock pulse then moves this level into the first cell of the shift register. The correct state for the second bit is placed on the Data Input and another clock pulse is generated. This moves the new data into the first cell of the shift register, and the original contents of this cell are moved to the second cell.

This process continues, with new bits being clocked into the chip and the existing ones being moved along the shift register. The outputs of the chip do not respond to the new data at this stage. They remain at their original states until all 32 bits of data have been clocked into the chip. A short pulse is then supplied to the Strobe Input, causing the bit pattern in the shift register to be transferred to and latched on the output pins. Another 32 bits of data are then clocked into the chip, another strobe pulse is used to latch the new data onto the outputs, and so on. In addition to giving a "clean" transition from one word of data to the next, the strobe pulse also ensures that the serial link does not stay out of synchronisation if a glitch occurs in the system.

Software

Listing 3 is a GW BASIC or QBASIC program that will output eight bits of data to port D. I have settled for eight bits of data in order to keep the listing reasonably short, but the basic method of operation is the same whether you need to output one bit or all 32 bits. The program starts with an INPUT instruction, and this is used to supply a value that is output to port D. There is no error trapping in the program, so make sure you always enter an integer from 0 to 255. The value you enter is placed in variable A, and this value has to be examined on a bit by bit basis so that the correct bit pattern can be output on the data line. Line 30 uses a bitwise AND instruction to determine the state of bit 0. Variable B will have a value of 1 or 0, depending on whether this bit is at 1 or 0.

Having ascertained the state of bit 0, the Data Input must be set at the corresponding logic level. A clock pulse is then generated so that this bit is moved into the shift register. First variable C is set at a value of 7 or 3 depending on whether bit 0 is high or low. This value is then sent to the handshake output of the printer port at &H37A. Obviously this address must be changed in the relevant program lines if you are not using a port that has &H378 as its base address. Note that the value sent to the handshake outputs is not simply 0 or 1, because all three lines that are used must be set at the correct states. Initially, the Strobe and Clock Input terminal of the UCN5818AF must be low, which due to the inverters on these lines requires a value of 3 to be sent to the port. This value is boosted to 7 if the (non-inverted) output driving the Data Input must be set high.

Next the clock pulse must be generated, and this is achieved by first writing a value to the port that is 2 less than the existing value ($C - 2$). Then the port is returned to its original value. The program then moves on to bit 1, and its state is determined by bitwise ANDing the value in variable A with a masking number of 2. The returned value is 0 if this bit is low or 2 if it is high. The same process as before is then used to set the Data Input to the correct level and generate the clock pulse. Essentially the same process is used to determine the states of bits 2 to 7 and to clock the correct logic levels into the shift register. Lines 590 and 600 then generate a strobe pulse so that the bit pattern in the shift register is transferred to the outputs of the UCN5818AF. Finally, line 610 loops the program back to the Input instruction so that a new value can be entered. Use the normal Control-Break combination to break out of the program.

Back to front

The program includes eight PRINT instructions that print the value of B after each bitwise AND operation. This helps to show how the program works, and the bit pattern contained in the printed values should be reflected in the logic levels on the outputs of Port D. Of course, these instructions are not needed in real world applications. If you try this program you will notice that the functions of the eight outputs so not agree with those shown in Figure 3.21. What should be bit 0 acts as bit 7, what should be bit 1 acts as bit 6, and so on. This demonstrates the point that the function of each output terminal is controlled by software and is not governed by the hardware.

In order to get the system to agree with the line assignments of Figure 3.21 it is merely necessary to change the software so that bit 7 is checked and clocked out first, running through to bit 0 at the end. You can use as many or as few of the output terminals as you like, and the software controls their functions. If you need 32 individual output lines, one 32-bit port, or any other combination, with the appropriate software the hardware will duly oblige.

Listing 3

```
10 REM UCN5818AF 8-bit program
20 INPUT A
30 B = (A AND 1)
40 PRINT B
50 IF B = 1 THEN C = 7
60 IF B = 0 THEN C = 3
70 OUT &H37A,C
80 OUT &H37A,(C - 2)
```

```
90 OUT &H37A,C
100 B = (A AND 2)
110 PRINT B
120 IF B = 2 THEN C = 7
130 IF B = 0 THEN C = 3
140 OUT &H37A,C
150 OUT &H37A,(C - 2)
160 OUT &H37A,C
170 B = (A AND 4)
180 PRINT B
190 IF B = 4 THEN C = 7
200 IF B = 0 THEN C = 3
210 OUT &H37A,C
220 OUT &H37A,(C - 2)
230 OUT &H37A,C
240 B = (A AND 8)
250 PRINT B
260 IF B = 8 THEN C = 7
270 IF B = 0 THEN C = 3
280 OUT &H37A,C
290 OUT &H37A,(C - 2)
300 OUT &H37A,C
310 B = (A AND 16)
320 PRINT B
330 IF B = 16 THEN C = 7
340 IF B = 0 THEN C = 3
350 OUT &H37A,C
360 OUT &H37A,(C - 2)
370 OUT &H37A,C
380 B = (A AND 32)
390 PRINT B
400 IF B = 32 THEN C = 7
410 IF B = 0 THEN C = 3
420 OUT &H37A,C
430 OUT &H37A,(C - 2)
440 OUT &H37A,C
450 B = (A AND 64)
460 PRINT B
```

Fig.3.23 A switch box enables two devices to share a single parallel port

```
470 IF B = 64 THEN C = 7
480 IF B = 0 THEN C = 3
490 OUT &H37A,C
500 OUT &H37A,(C - 2)
510 OUT &H37A,C
520 B = (A AND 128)
530 PRINT B
540 IF B = 128 THEN C = 7
550 IF B = 0 THEN C = 3
560 OUT &H37A,C
570 OUT &H37A,(C - 2)
580 OUT &H37A,C
590 OUT &H37A,2
600 OUT &H37A,3
610 GOTO 20
```

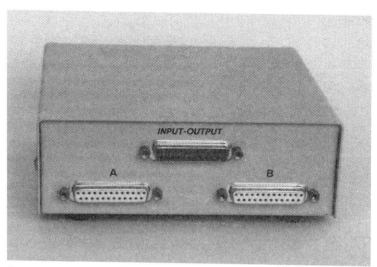

Fig.3.24 Rear view of the switch box showing the input and output
connectors

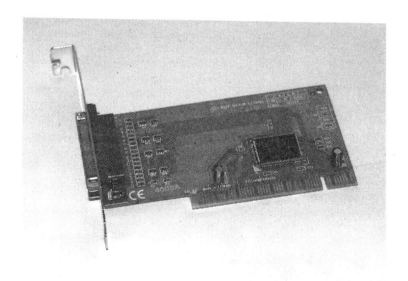

Fig.3.25 A PCI printer port expansion card

Fig.3.26 An ISA printer port expansion card

Adding a printer port

Most PCs are equipped with a printer port as standard, but unlike PC serial ports, there is usually just the one. This is not a problem if you have the printer connected to a USB port, but it is a problem if the printer port is needed for its primary purpose. It is possible to use a switch-box (Figures 3.23 and 3.24) to permit the port to be used with either a printer or your own add-on devices. In use this is not a very convenient way of handling things, and it is easy to leave the switch at the wrong setting. You might find the printer producing pages of garbage or your add-on "going bananas" because the switch is at the wrong setting.

Where possible, it is probably best to opt for a second port provided by an expansion card. PCI and ISA printer port cards are shown in Figures 3.25 and 3.26 respectively. It should be possible to add one of these

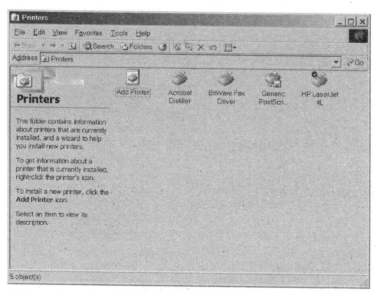

Fig.3.27 The Printers window shows all the installed printers

provided your PC has at least one spare PCI or ISA expansion slot. When you have the choice, it is usually deemed better to opt for a PCI card rather than an ISA card. A printer port card for use with you own add-ons is an exception to the rule, and it is probably better to opt for an ISA card if you PC has a free ISA slot. PCI cards have advantages such as proper Plug and Play capability, but they also have a major drawback in the current context. A PCI slot does not interface expansion cards direct onto the microprocessor's buses.

Instead, it acts more like a highly complex input/output port. The importance of this in a printer port context is that the port cannot occupy the normal addresses associated with this type of port. Instead, it must be controlled indirectly via the PCI circuitry. This is not of any consequence in its intended role as a printer port, because the expansion card should be supplied with Windows device drivers. These enable Windows to use the port correctly even though it is not a standard printer port.

There should be no problems if the software for your add-on project runs under Windows and controls the printer port via the operating system. However, in most cases direct accessing of the port is used,

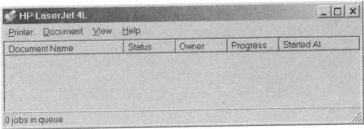

Fig.3.28 Use this window to launch the printer's properties window

and this will not work with a PCI card because it does not use the standard input/output addresses. There is no hardware to access at the normal port addresses. The Windows drivers only work when running the computer under Windows, and they will be of no use with another operating system such as MS-DOS.

Unfortunately, modern PCs tend to have only one ISA expansion slot or none at all. This gives no alternative to using a PCI expansion card and trying to find a way of utilising it. One way around the direct access problem is to use the PC's built-in port for your add-ons and the new card for the printer. The printer should work well using the new port and the device drivers supplied with the card. Your add-ons should work properly via the built-in printer port, which will have standard hardware at one of the normal address ranges. This method might not work if the device on the printer port is something other than a printer. Some external drives for example, require direct access to the printer port in order to operate at full speed. In most cases though, moving the printer or other device to the new port will enable everything to work properly.

Remember to alter the appropriate Windows setting so that programs can direct data for the printer to the correct port. Go to the Start menu and then select Settings followed by Printers. This launches the Printers window (Figure 3.27) where there should be an icon for your normal printer. Double-click on its icon, which will produce a small window like the one in Figure 3.28. Next, go to the Printer menu and select the Properties option. This brings up a window something like the one in Figure 3.29, but the printer's Properties window is to some extent customised to suit each printer. Therefore, the one for your printer will probably not be the same as the one shown here. Operate the tabs one by one and search each section for a menu that enables the printer's port to be selected (Figure 3.30). Select the appropriate port and then operate the Apply and OK buttons. All Windows programs should then output data for the printer to the appropriate port.

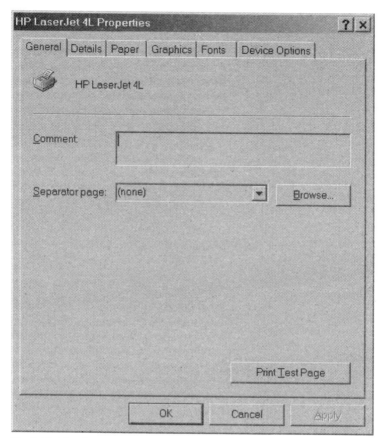

Fig.3.29 The General section of a typical printer properties window

Re-mapping

The expansion card might be supplied with a software solution in the form of a re-mapping program. This tries to intercept instructions that are directed at the standard port addresses. It then substitutes an appropriate routine to drive the PCI card. There is no guarantee that this type of thing will work properly, but it usually works well enough. One potential problem is that software often controls the hardware directly in order to obtain greater speed. This method of intercepting instructions and substituting appropriate routines might slow things down to an

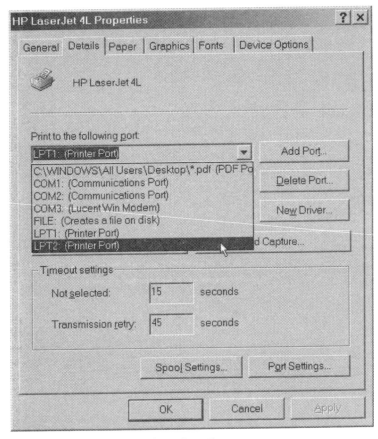

Fig.3.30 Select the required port from the menu

unacceptable degree. This does not seem to be a significant problem in practice, probably due to serial and parallel ports being quite slow in relation to the rest of the PC. Anyway, if you are going to use a re-mapping facility it is probably best to use the re-mapped port for your add-ons, with the built-in port being used for external drives, etc.

Note that a PCI card is unlikely to use the re-mapping facility by default. The card's device driver should have a properties window that enables the re-mapping to be enabled. This might be available by double clicking on the port's entry in Device Manager, but this often gives access to a cut down version of the properties window. Where this is the case, look for another entry for the card in Device Manager, in amongst the main categories. Double clicking on this entry should give access to the full properties window. If a re-mapping facility is provided, there should be a Configuration section or something similar (Figure 3.31). In this example, the re-mapping can be enabled by ticking the appropriate checkbox, and base addresses of &H278 and &H378 can be selected for the parallel port. Of course, the address selected must not be in use by another port. Where necessary, check the properties windows for the other ports to determine their base addresses, so that address conflicts can be avoided.

Points to remember

By using the handshake lines to provide an eight-bit input port, the data lines of the printer port are left for use as an output port. In this way the printer port can be "stretched" to provide both a "byte size" input and output.

The handshake inputs can be used to provide more than eight input lines, but things inevitably get a bit more involved as more inputs are added. There are probably better ways of handling things if more than 16 inputs are required.

Any modern PC should have a printer port that is capable of bidirectional operation. This means that the eight data lines can be switched to operate as inputs. If you only require an eight-bit input port plus a few handshake lines, this method is much easier than using the handshake lines to provide an eight-bit input. The software is simpler and no additional hardware is needed.

For basic bidirectional operation the printer port should be set for SPP or EPP operation. With a modern PC the printer port is normally controlled via the BIOS Setup program, rather than using switches or jumpers on the motherboard. The SPP mode is called "Standard" mode in some BIOS Setup programs. The ECP mode is unlikely to provide basic bidirectional operation.

Using a synchronous serial connection to an add-on circuit helps to reduce the number of wires in the link, and makes the best use of the available input/output lines. However, it complicates the software and is relatively slow.

In theory just two wires plus an earth line are needed for a synchronous serial link. In practice the system might slip out of synchronisation, or not get properly synchronised in the first place, unless a third wire is used.

TTL and CMOS shift registers can be used as the basis of a synchronous serial link, but there are special computer chips designed for this type of interfacing. In general, it is better to use these chips when suitable devices can be located.

Where possible, add an extra parallel port using an ISA expansion card rather than a PCI type. A PCI type will be of limited use unless it has a re-mapping facility that permits it to mimic a standard parallel port. The re-mapping facility is unlikely to be enabled by default, so you will have to switch it on and select a suitable base address.

Serial port interfacing

8-bit I/O

Most PCs have at least one spare serial port, which makes this seem like a good way of interfacing a PC to your add-on devices. In practice using a serial port tends to be far less straightforward than interfacing an equivalent circuit to a parallel port. Where possible I would certainly recommend using a printer port or an add-on parallel port for your PC based projects. The main problem with a serial port is that it can not directly provide parallel data, or read it. A certain amount of interfacing is needed in order to accomplish the serial to parallel and parallel to serial conversions. You therefore need a fair amount of circuitry in addition to the basic hardware for your add-on.

Another point to bear in mind is that this additional circuitry only provides basic eight-bit input and eight-bit output ports with no handshake lines. There are actually handshake inputs and outputs on the serial port which can be used to control the flow of data into and out of the port, and in some circumstances it might be possible to use these as part of the handshake set-up for your add-on device. There may also be inputs and outputs available on the serial interface device that can be used as part of the handshake system for your add-on. In general though, it is best to keep any handshaking to the bare minimum.

Of course, by utilising multiplexing techniques it is possible to provide virtually any desired number of input and output lines using a serial port, but this further complicates matters. It is easy to end up with a circuit that is 90 percent serial encoding, decoding, and multiplexing and 10 percent the actual add-on device!

Another problem with a standard RS232C interface is that it is relatively slow. Using the standard transmission rates, data can only be sent at about one or two kilobytes per second. This compares to rates of around

500 kilobytes per second or more for parallel interfaces. In fact a modern parallel port in an enhanced mode can manage data transfers at up to 2 megabytes per second. This relative lack of speed is not always of importance, but it does render an RS232C interface impractical for certain applications. It is usually possible to use a PC serial port at speeds beyond the normal standards, but this only speeds things up by a factor of six.

It should be pointed out that serial interfaces do have two or three advantages. Firstly, they are truly bidirectional, and all PC serial ports have the ability to both send and receive bytes of data. A serial port can also be used with long connecting cables, whereas parallel ports are normally restricted to quite short leads. In fact an ordinary PC parallel printer port should not be used with a connecting cable more than about two or three metres long. Somewhat greater ranges can be achieved using special low capacitance cables, but around 15 metres is the normal maximum.

The maximum cable length for an RS232C serial port depends on the rate at which data is transferred, but cables of around 10 to 20 metres are normally satisfactory at the higher rates. Greater ranges can be achieved using high quality cables. In theory at any rate, cables of a kilometre or more are acceptable at the lower transfer speeds. Another advantage of serial interfacing is that only simple connecting cables are required. A basic two-way system requires just three connecting cables, and only five wires are needed if hardware handshaking is utilised. This compares to 17 wires for a basic two-way parallel system with no handshaking.

Bit-By-Bit

A serial interface sends all eight bits of data over a single line, and it must therefore send bits one at a time. This is the reason that serial interfaces tend to be relatively slow. A parallel interface transfers whole bytes at a time whereas a serial type literally transfers data on a bit-by-bit basis. A normal RS232C serial interface is asynchronous, which means that there are no additional connecting wires carrying a clock signal or some other form of synchronisation signal. The transmitting and receiving circuits must, of course, be kept correctly synchronised somehow. Synchronisation is achieved by using standard transmission rates and sending additional bits with each byte of data.

The two example waveforms of Figure 4.1 show how this system operates. The first point to note here is that the signal voltages are not at any form

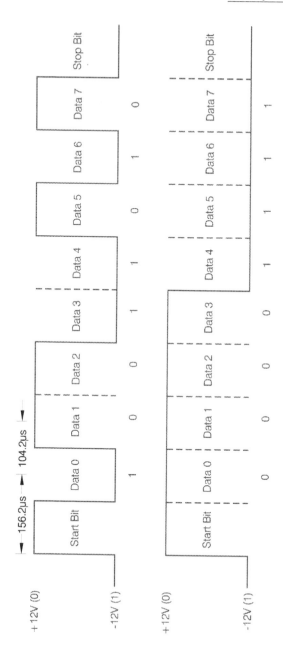

Fig.4.1 Example waveforms for two serial bytes at a bate of 9600 baud

of standard 5-volt logic levels, but are instead at plus and minus 12 volts. In fact the signal voltages can be as low as 3 volts when fully loaded, but would more usually be at around eight to ten volts. Serial interface chips do actually operate at normal logic levels, but they interface to the RS232C connector via special line drivers and receivers. These provide level shifting so that the interface operates at the correct voltage levels, and they also provide an inversion. Hence positive and negative voltages respectively represent logic 0 and logic 1, which is the opposite of what one might expect.

RS232C serial interfaces operate at a number of standard transmission rates, or baud rates as they are known. The baud rate is simply the number of bits sent per second if there is a continuous data stream. All the standard baud rates are listed here:

50	75	110	150
300	600	1200	2400
4800	9600	19200	

Unless you need to use very long connecting cables it is advisable to use one of the higher baud rates as these provide higher maximum transfer rates. By electronic and computing standards the maximum rate at which data can be transferred is quite low even at the higher baud rates. Including the synchronisation signals there are typically ten bits transmitted per byte, which means that baud rates of 9600 and 19200 provide maximum data transfer rates of just 960 and 1920 bytes per second.

This is sufficient for many applications, but is totally inadequate for something like audio digitising. Bear in mind that there is a small delay between the commencement of data being sent and a fully decoded byte appearing at the receiving device. Using a high baud rate keeps this delay as small s possible (a little over 100 µs at 9600 baud).

The synchronisation signals are called stop and start bits, which are, as one would expect, sent immediately before and after the data bits. The start bit indicates to the receiving circuit that it must sample the signal line after a certain period of time, and this time is equal to the period of 1.5 bits. In the example of Figure 4.1 the transmission rate is 9600 baud, which works out at approximately 104.2 µs per bit (1000000 µs divided by 9600 baud equals 104.2 µs). Sampling the input line after 156.2 µs

(1.5 bits) therefore results in the logic level being tested in the middle of the first bit. This is always the least significant bit (D0).

The input line is then tested every 104.2 µs until bits D1 through to D7 have been read into the receiver register. The data line is then returned to its standby state for 104.2 µs to produce the stop bit, which really just provides a guaranteed minimum gap from one byte of data to the next. This gives the receiving device time to deal with one byte of data before it starts to receive the next one.

Word formats

The serial signal in this example has one start bit, eight data bits, one stop bit, and no parity checking, which is probably the most common word format. However, there are many others in use, with anything from five to eight data bits, one, one and a half, or two stop bits, and odd or even parity checking. There is always a single start bit incidentally. In the present context you will normally require eight-bit data transfers, and there is no point in using anything less than an eight-bit word format. Normally it is better to use one rather than two stop bits because this gives a slightly faster maximum transfer rate, but two stop bits can be used if your add-on circuit needs a little extra time to process one byte of data before the next is received.

Parity checking is a simple method of error checking that relies on an extra bit being sent at the end of bytes, where necessary, so that there is always an even or an odd number of bits. This method of checking is not very reliable since a double glitch can result in data being corrupted but the parity being left intact. It is little used in practice and I would recommend avoiding word formats that involve either type of parity checking.

Serial interfaces have a reputation for being difficult to deal with, and this is at least partially due to the numerous baud rates and word formats in use. It is not simply enough to get the transmitting and receiving devices connected together correctly. Unless both ends of the system are set up to use the same word format and baud rate it is unlikely that the system will function correctly. It will certainly fail to operate at all if the sending and receiving baud rates are different. Always make sure that both ends of the system are set to the same word format and baud rate. If a serial system fails to transfer data correctly always recheck that the transmitting and receiving circuits are set up correctly.

Fig.4.2 Pinout details for the 6402 UART

UART

It is probably not that difficult to decode a serial signal using a circuit based on a shift register, but there are numerous devices available that provide the necessary decoding and control hardware. Many of these devices are designed to operate on the bus of a microprocessor and are not really suitable for operation in most PC add-ons. For serial interfacing to a non-microprocessor-based add-on it is a UART (universal asynchronous receiver/transmitter) that is required. The industry standard UART is the 6402, which can handle any standard word format and baud rate. This is a 40-pin device which has the pinout configuration shown in Figure 4.2.

As the UART name suggests, both serial-to-parallel and parallel-to-serial conversion are catered for. The device has tristate outputs that can be directly interfaced to the busses of many microprocessors, as can its inputs. It works equally well in normal logic circuits with the outputs permanently enabled and the inputs either hard-wired or controlled via standard logic circuits. The important point here is that it does not require a microprocessor and a software routine in order to set the required word format. Simply connecting a few inputs to the correct logic levels is all that is needed in order to perform this task.

Pins 34 to 39 control the word format, and pin 34 is the control register load input. A high level on pin 34 loads the control register and it can simply be wired permanently to logic one if the other control inputs are to be hard-wired. The functions of the other control pins are as follows:

Pin 35, Parity Inhibit

A high level on this input inhibits parity generation during transmission, and switches off parity checking during reception.

PIN 36, Stop Bit Select

Setting this input high selects two stop bits (1.5 for five data bit formats). With this input set low the word format has one stop bit.

Pins 37 and 38, Character Length Select 1/2

These two inputs select the word length (the number of data bits) as per this table;

Word Length	CLS1	CLS2
5 bits	Low	Low
6 bits	High	Low
7 bits	Low	High
8 bits	High	High

Pin 39, Even Parity Enable

This input is set high for even parity or low for odd parity. Note that this input has no effect if pin 35 (parity inhibit) is set high and parity is disabled.

The word control inputs are common to both the transmitter and receiver sections of the 6402, but there are separate clock inputs. The transmitter clock input is at pin 40 and the receiver clock input is at pin 17. In both cases the clock frequency must be 16 times the required baud rate and must not exceed 3.2MHz. This enables baud rates of up to 200000 (200 kilobaud) to be accommodated, which is far more than adequate for normal requirements. Even if you set a PC serial port to operate at a higher than normal rate a 6402 UART should be able to cope.

Pin 21 is the master reset input, and this must be supplied with a positive pulse at switch-on in order to ensure that the chip initialises correctly. In comparison to most chips a fairly long reset pulse is needed, but a simple C - R network is still sufficient. The positive and 0-volt supplies connect to pins one and three respectively. The 6402 will actually operate over a supply voltage range of four to 10 volts (four to 6.5 volts for the 6402C), but it will normally be operated from a standard 5-volt supply. It is based on CMOS technology and the supply current therefore depends on the clock frequency, but the supply current is usually less than two milliamps.

Receiver

The input data, which must be at normal 5-volt logic levels, is fed to the receiver register input at pin 21. Decoded bytes appear on the eight receiver buffer register outputs at pins five (most significant) to 12 (least significant). These are tristate inputs that are controlled by the receiver register disable input (pin four). The outputs go to the high-impedance state when pin four is taken high. This facility is not usually needed and pin four is then connected to ground so that the receiver outputs are permanently enabled.

When a new byte of data is received the data received flag at pin 19 goes high. A low pulse applied to the data received reset input at pin 18 can be used to reset this flag. In many applications these inputs are not needed, because the main add-on circuit will automatically respond to new bytes of data as and when they are received. For example, feeding fresh data to a digital-to-analogue converter results in it altering its output to suit without the need for any control signals such as a strobe pulse. Not all circuits are so accommodating though, and in some cases a signal is needed to indicate that fresh data is available.

As an example, in some applications data might be sent in (say) groups of three bytes, and the receiving circuit then needs some means of counting in the bytes so that it knows which byte is which, and when all three have been received. This requires a strobe pulse each time a fresh byte has been received. Using the data received flag to reset itself can produce this signal. All that is needed is an inverter and a short delay circuit connected between the data received flag and its reset input. A strobe pulse is then generated each time a fresh byte of data is placed on the outputs.

There are three error flags available at pins 13 to 15, and these respectively indicate a parity error, a framing error (an incorrect stop bit or first stop bit), and an overrun error. The latter occurs when a new byte of data is fully decoded before the data received flag has been reset. These outputs can be used to operate warning LEDs or something of this nature, but in most cases you will be all too aware if something goes wrong with the decoding process, rendering the warning LEDs of little practical use.

Transmitter

On the transmitter side of things the eight bits of parallel data are supplied to the transmitter buffer register inputs at pins 26 (least significant) to 33 (most significant). In order to transmit the data the transmitter buffer register load input at pin 23 must be pulsed low. As with most serial devices, a system of buffering is utilised, with the data being transferred to the buffer register on the high to low transition, and then into the transmitter register on the low to high transition. If the transmitter register is full the second transfer is delayed until it is empty. This still leaves the possibility of overwriting a byte of data in the transmitter buffer register.

One way of avoiding this is to use a timing circuit to ensure that data can not be written to the interface at an excessive rate. Another is to use the two handshake outputs available on the 6402. These are the transmitter buffer register empty (pin 22) and the transmitter register empty (pin 24) flags, both of which go high when their respective registers are empty. These flags, and those of the receiver section, are tristate types. They are all set to the high-impedance state by taking the status flag disable input (pin 16) high, or enabled by taking this input low. The serial data stream is provided on the transmitter register output at pin 25, and this operates at normal 5-volt logic levels.

Receiver circuit

Figure 4.3 shows the circuit diagram for a simple serial-to-parallel converter based on the 6402 UART. The crystal oscillator based on TR1 generates the clock signal, and this operates at 2.4576MHz. The baud rate provided by the UART is one sixteenth of this frequency, which works out at a baud rate of 153,600 baud. A baud rate of 9600 is needed, which requires the 2.4576MHz signal to be divided by 16. This division is provided by the first four stages of IC1, which is a CMOS 4024BE seven-stage binary counter. Using other outputs of IC1 can provide these additional baud rates:

Output (pin no.)	Baud Rate
Q3 (9)	19200
Q5 (5)	4800
Q6 (4)	2400
Q7 (3)	1200

Special line receivers are available, but unless long connecting cables are used a simple transistor inverter stage is all that is needed to provide the inversion and level shifting at the serial input. This is the function of TR2. C4 and R6 provide the reset pulse to the UART (IC2) at switch-on. The control register inputs are hard wired for a word format of eight data bits, one stop bit, and no parity checking, but you can obviously change the wiring to produce any required format. However, this word format is the most common one these days, and there is no point in using a different one unless you really do need a different word format for some reason.

The decoded bytes of data are produced on outputs D0 to D7, and are at 5-volt CMOS logic levels. In practice they also seem to drive 74LS** logic devices properly, but would probably have insufficient drive currents to drive standard TTL devices (which are now obsolete anyway). TR3 inverts the output signal from the data received flag and uses it to reset this flag by way of the data received reset input. This produces an output pulse each time fresh data appears on the outputs. C5 stretches the low output pulse that is produced at the collector of TR3. This stretching will not always be required, and if continuous streams of data are used it might be necessary to reduce the value of C5 to around 47n.

Transmitter circuit

Figure 4.4 shows the circuit diagram for the parallel to serial converter. The clock circuit is identical to the one used in the receiver circuit, and in

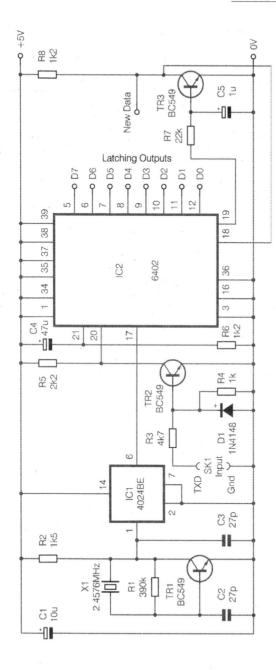

Fig.4.3 The circuit diagram for the serial receiver. The clock circuit provides operation at 9600 baud, but other rates are supported

a transmitter/receiver circuit it is perfectly all right to use the same clock circuit for both sections of the unit provided they are to operate at the same baud rate. C4 and R7 provide the reset pulse at switch-on, and in a transmitter receiver circuit these will be common to both sections of the unit, as will IC2 itself. The control inputs of IC2 are programmed to produce a word format of eight data bits, one stop bit and no parity checking. They can be reconfigured to produce other formats, but remember that in a two-way system the reception and transmission word formats have to be the same.

The line driver consists of a simple transistor inverter stage based on TR2. This does not provide proper RS232C signal voltages, which require minimum loaded drive potentials of plus and minus 3 volts. This circuit provides drive voltages of 0 and +5 volts. In practice the lack of a true negative output level does not normally stop an RS232C interface from working, and it avoids the need for plus and minus 12-volt supplies. However, proper operation without the correct drive potentials can not be guaranteed, and it is unlikely to work when using long connecting cables. It is certainly worth trying though, as it greatly simplifies things in circumstances where it will work. If your application requires a proper line driver, refer to the section of this chapter that deals with line driver and receiver devices.

In order to transmit a byte of data the TBRL input of IC2 must be pulsed low, and this function must be provided by some control logic in the main add-on circuit. For reliable operation the data on the input lines must be stable immediately prior to and during the pulse on TBRL. This pulse can be quite short, but it is probably best to err on the side of caution and use a pulse that is about one UART clock cycle in length. The transmitter register is loaded on the rising edge at the end of the pulse, and transmission then commences.

It is important that data is not written to the serial interface at an excessive rate. In many applications this will not be a problem, with only the odd byte of data be sent to the interface here and there. The real problem occurs where bursts of data will be handled by the interface, even if each data bust only consists of three or four bytes.

There are two ways of handling the problem, and one of these is to design the control logic of the main circuit to regulate the flow of data, and prevent bytes from being sent at an excessive rate. Where this approach can be implemented reasonably easily it will almost certainly represent the best approach to the problem. The other method is to use one of the handshake outputs of the UART to provide a hold-off so that

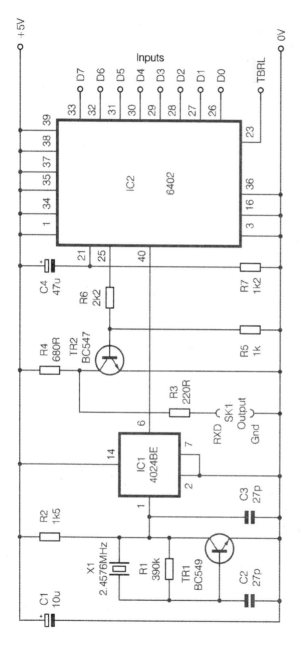

Fig.4.4 The serial transmitter circuit. It does not provide full RS232C output levels

data can not be sent to the interface at a rate it can not handle. It will probably not matter whether the TRE (pin 24) or TBRE (pin 22) output is used, and in either case data should not be written to the interface unless the handshake output is high.

Connections

The normal connector for an RS232C interface is a 25-pin D type, but many PCs have the AT style 9-pin connector. In both cases the connector on the computer is a male connector, and you require a female type to make the connections to the port. Figure 4.5 provides connection details for both types of PC serial port. Where possible, which in practice is actually the vast majority of cases, no form of handshaking should be used.

A serial interface is slow by normal computing standards, and very slow by general electronic standards. Consequently, when sending data to an add-on via a serial interface the add-on should be able to handle a continuous flow of data. Similarly, even an old PC with a relatively slow processor should be able to process a continuous flow of data without difficulty. With no handshaking used the interconnections are very simple, and it is just a matter of the two input or output leads of the interface to the corresponding terminals of the PC's RS232C port.

There is a possible complication in that some PCs are reluctant to send data unless the handshake inputs are held at the level that indicates the receiving device is ready for action. For some reason this may even "gum the works" when the PC is set to use software handshaking or no handshaking at all. The root of the problem is that handshake inputs may assume the hold-off state if they are simply left floating. A simple solution that usually works is to cross-couple the serial port's handshake lines. In practice this means connecting the clear to send (CTS) and data set ready (DSR) inputs to the request to send (RTS) and data terminal ready (DTR) outputs respectively. If that fails to free things up, try connecting the ring indicator input to one of the handshake outputs as well.

On the face of it there is no reason for having two sets of handshake lines, since one set is all that is needed to control the flow of data. The usual scheme of things, if both sets are actually operational, is to have CTS and RTS to control the flow of data, with DTR and DSR indicating whether or not the receiving device is actually operational. If a serial printer is off-line because it is out of paper for example, this would be indicated via DTR and DSR.

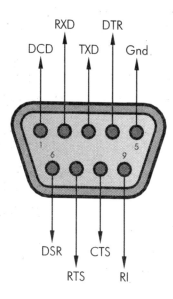

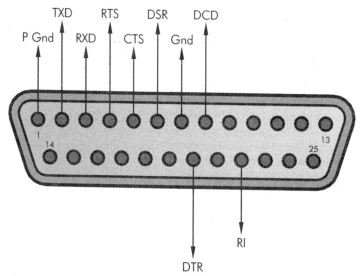

Fig.4.5 Connection details for both types of PC serial port

The CTS and RTS lines would be used to control the flow of data when the printer was on-line. In reality the way in which the handshake lines are used varies somewhat from one serial device to another, and serial links will sometimes only function if they are connected in what is theoretically the wrong manner. It is mainly for this reason that hardware handshaking is best avoided where possible. Where it is implemented it often results in a try everything until it works approach.

Software handshaking

You may come across references to software handshaking, or XON/XOFF handshaking, as it is also known. This is where the handshaking is controlled via software codes sent from the receiving device to the transmitting device via a data link. With this type of handshaking you therefore need a full-duplex (two-way) link even though data is only being sent in one direction (half-duplex operation). The ASCII codes 17 and 19 are normally used for XON (switch on) and XOFF (switch off) respectively.

In theory it is not necessary to have the handshake lines coupled together, but in practice the sending device may refuse to send anything unless its handshake inputs are at the "on" voltage. Presumably it decides that the receiving device is off-line and refuses to start transmitting until it gets the appropriate input level on one or both of its handshake inputs. It would obviously be possible to use this type of handshaking with your own projects, but it would seem to be doing things the hard way. Also, this method is not noted for its reliability, so if handshaking is deemed absolutely necessary it is best to adopt the hardware method.

DCE and DTE

You might also encounter references to DCE and DTE when dealing with serial interfacing. These respectively stand for data communications equipment and data terminal equipment. In theory a serial link normally consists of a DCE device and a DTE type. A computer is normally the device that controls the system, and would be a DTE unit. Something like a printer or one of your add-ons would normally be the controlled device, or the DCE unit in serial interfacing terminology. The difference between the two types is that DTE units transmit on their "TXD" outputs and receive on their "RXD" inputs.

Things are done the other way round with DCE units, which transmit on their "RXD" lines and receive on their "TXD" lines. The handshake lines are also swapped over so that inputs become outputs and vice versa. This may seem to be pointless and potentially confusing, and I suppose that a good case to this effect could be made. Apparently the reason for having the two categories of equipment is that it enables a so-called "straight" connecting cable to be used. In other words, the cable connects pin one at one end to pin one at the other, pin two to pin two, and so on. Connecting two DCE units together, or two DTE types, requires the correct method of cross coupling for successful operation. For example, pin two at one end has to connect to pin three at the other in order to provide a data link.

When you are constructing your own serial units there should be no confusion about the method of connection. A PC is a DTE device, and it does things in the logical way with data output from "TXD" and received on "RXD". In the circuits of Figures 4.3 and 4.4 the labelling on the input and output sockets shows the terminals of the PC serial ports that the lines connect to incidentally.

Line drivers/receivers

As pointed out previously, it is often possible to use simple inverters rather than proper RS232C line drivers and receivers. However, if you are using long connecting cables it is best to opt for the real thing, and clearly it is also necessary to fit proper line drivers to your projects when faced with a PC that will not work reliably with reduced drive voltages. The standard line drivers and receivers are the MC1488P and MC1489P respectively. These are both quad devices, but any unwanted sections can simply be left unused. Pinout details for both devices are provided in Figure 4.6.

Three of the line drivers in the MC1488P have two inputs, and effectively operate as NAND gates having outputs at line voltages. In most applications the gate capability is not required and either the two inputs of each driver must be driven in parallel, or the unused input must be tied high. The line receivers of the MC1489P each have a control input that can be used to alter the input threshold level, and it also has possible application in counteracting certain types of noise. In most cases though the control inputs are left unused.

One slight problem with the MC1489P is that it requires dual balanced 12-volt supplies in order to provide the correct output potentials. It would often be more convenient if a single 5-volt positive supply could be used. One solution to the problem is to use a switch mode power supply circuit

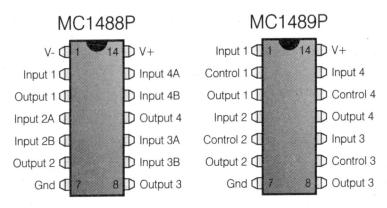

*Fig.4.6 Pinout details for the MC1488P and MC1489P line driver and
receiver chips*

to produce dual balanced 12-volt rails from a 5-volt supply. An alternative
is to use a device such as the MAX202, which is effectively a standard
dual line driver plus a built-in switch mode power supply circuit. This
enables it to produce adequate output potentials from a standard 5-volt
logic supply.

As an added bonus the MAX202 also includes a couple of line receivers.
The circuit diagram for a dual line driver/receiver based on the MAX202
appears in Figure 4.7. The switch mode power supply is a simple
capacitive pump type, and no inductors are required. The five capacitors
must be high quality types suitable for use in switching circuits, and
tantalum capacitors are probably the best choice.

Making Contact

Any high level language should have built-in support for the PC's serial
ports. Unfortunately, this support is usually slanted towards the sending
and receiving of files rather than byte-by-byte operation. You can, of
course, send a one-byte file to a serial port, but there will probably be
another byte or bytes sent with the data byte, such as an end of file
marker. The hardware in your add-on has to be designed to take this
sort of thing into account. Similarly, when sending serial data to a PC's
serial port it may be necessary to include additional bytes to help the
software digest the data properly.

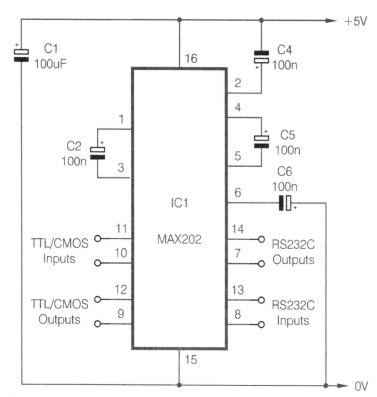

*Fig.4.7 A line driver and receiver circuit that requires a single
         +5-volt supply*

Where the programming language you are using supports direct port
access you can try controlling the serial port hardware directly. This is
not too difficult when sending data, where it is basically just a matter of
writing the data to the appropriate input/output address. A timing loop
can be used to ensure that data is not written to the port at an excessive
rate, or you could try reading the appropriate status flag of the chip.
Reading data direct from a serial port is much trickier, since the operating
system will be dealing with bytes of data as and when they arrive. This is
almost invariably achieved via interrupt routines. You must not use
software routines that compete with the operating system. Unless you
really know what you are doing, direct reading of the serial port is not a
practical proposition.

The serial ports are written to and read at the base address of the port. These are the four serial port base addresses, but note that under certain circumstances the operating system might shuffle the ports into a slightly different scheme of things (ports two and four having their address ranges swapped over for example). This table also shows the IRQ numbers for each port.

Port	Base Address	IRQ
One	3F8	4
Two	2F8	3
Three	3E8	4
Four	2E8	3

Direct control of a serial port, other than the data register, can be a slightly "hit and miss" affair as there have been several serial interface chips used in PCs over the years. However, they are to a large extent compatible, and you are unlikely to encounter major problems to due to a lack chip compatibility. The original PCs used an 8250 chip, but most recent PCs have used the 16550, or a variant of this device. In fact modern PCs have a single chip to handle the basic input/output functions, and this chip includes a section that is functionally the same as a device from the 16550 family. Anyway, this is the "standard" scheme of things for the serial port registers.

Address	R/W	Register	DLAB
Base	Read	Received Data	0
Base	Write	Data To Transmit	0
Base	R/W	Clock Divider Latch (LSB)	1
Base + 1	R/W	Clock Divider Latch (MSB)	1
Base + 1	Write	Interrupt Enable Register	0
Base + 2	Read	Interrupt Identification Register	
Base + 3	R/W	Line Control Register	
Base + 4	R/W	Modem Control Register	

Base + 5   Read   Line Status Register

Base + 6   Read   Modem Status Register

Base + 7   -   Reserved

There is a slight complication in that two registers have different functions depending on the setting of the divisor latch access bit (DLAB), which is bit seven of the line control register. This bit must be set to 0 to gain access to the data registers and the interrupt enable register, and to 1 to access the two clock divider latches.

It can be useful to control the divider latches directly as they permit the baud rate to be controlled. The clock for the serial chip is at a frequency of 1.8432MHz, but there is an internal division by 16 so that the baud rate is one sixteenth of this figures (115.2 kilobaud). Placing a divisor into the clock divider latches, which together hold a 16-bit value, can reduce the baud rate further. This gives a division range of 1 to 65535. The baud rate of a serial port can usually be set via the operating system, and can be set using the built-in facilities of some programming languages. However, direct control offers a simple but effective alternative.

It also enables the use of any baud rate supported by the hardware, rather than restricting you to the standard rates. Using a value of zero for the MSB and one for the LSB provides a baud rate of 115.2 kilobaud, and permits substantially faster data transfers than the highest standard rate of 19.2 kilobaud. Data can be transferred at over 11k per second using this rate. This is still quite slow by parallel port standards, but it is more than adequate for most applications. It has to be pointed out that not all PC serial ports are guaranteed to work at 115.2 kilobaud, but the serial ports of any reasonably modern PC should be able to do so.

Interrupts

The interrupt enable register is reasonably straightforward, and the functions of each bit are detailed in this table:

Bit   Function

0   Received Data Available

1   Transmitter Holding Register Empty

2	Receiver Line Status
3	Modem Status
4	Enables Sleep Mode (only if 16750 UART fitted)
5	Enables Low Power Mode (only if 16750 UART fitted)
6	Reserved
7	Reserved

In each case setting a bit high enables that form of interrupt. With bit 0 set high an interrupt is generated when the receiving register has a fresh byte of data available. The easiest way of directly reading the port is probably to disable this interrupt and use polling instead. Polling simply means frequent testing of the appropriate status flag, with the port being read when it indicates fresh data is available. This method is less efficient in that it involves more work for the processor, but with the received data interrupt disabled it should avoid conflicts with the operating system. Bit 1 produces an interrupt when the transmitter register is empty and the chip is ready to receive a new byte of data for transmission. Again, it is probably easiest to disable this interrupt and rely on polling or timing loops to prevent data being written to the port at an excessive rate. Bits 2 and 3 enable receiver line status and modem status interrupts, which you will probably have no need to implement.

When bit 0 of the interrupt identification register is at 0 an interrupt is pending, and bits 1 and 2 identify the pending interrupt with the highest priority in this fashion:

Bit 2	Bit 1	Priority	Source
0	0	Fourth	Modem Status
0	1	Third	Transmitter Register
1	0	Second	Receiver Data
1	1	First	Receiver Line Status

Word control

The line control register controls the word format for reception and transmission. This is a summary of the bit functions:

Bits 0 and 1

These set the number of data bits as follows:

Bit 0	Bit 1	Word Length
0	0	5
0	1	6
1	0	7
1	1	8

Bit 2

This bit is set low for one stop bit or high for two stop bits (1.5 stop bits for five data bit operation)

Bit 3

The parity enable bit. Set to 1 to enable parity or 0 to disable parity checking.

Bit 4

This bit selects the type of parity checking used, but obviously has no effect if parity is disabled via bit 3. Set this bit to 1 for even parity or 0 for odd parity.

Bit 5

The stuck parity bit.

Bit 6

The set break control bit. Set to 0 for normal operation, or to 1 to force the serial output pin of the chip to logic 0.

Bit 7

Divisor Latch Access Bit (DLAB).

Modem control

The modem control register is used primarily to control the data terminal ready (bit 0) and request to send (bit 1) handshake outputs. In both cases logic 0 sets the output to the standby state and logic 1 sets it to the active state. Bit 4 provides a loopback feature for diagnostic testing.

Line status

The line status register enables various status flags to be read. This is a summary of the bit functions:

Bit 0

This is the received data ready flag, and it is set high when a complete character has been received and transferred to the receiver buffer register. Writing a 0 to it can reset this bit, but it is reset automatically when the received data is read.

Bit 1

This is the overrun flag, and it is set to 1 when a byte of data is placed in the receiver buffer register before the previous byte was read. It is reset when the line status register is read.

Bit 2

Bit 2 is set to 1 when a parity error is detected. It is reset when the line status register is read.

Bit 3

The framing error bit. When it is set to 1 the last character received did not have a valid stop bit.

Bit 4

This is the break interrupt indicator. It is set at 1 when the received data input is held at logic 0 for more than the duration of one complete character including start and stop bits, etc.

Bits 0 to 4 are all error flags, and any of these being activated causes a line status interrupt to be generated.

Bit 5

The transmitter holding register empty bit. This flag is set to 0 when the processor loads the transmitter holding register and to 1 when a character is transferred from the holding register to the transmitter register. In other words, when set to 1 it indicates that the transmitter holding register is ready to receive another byte of data. It also generates an interrupt request.

Bit 6

This is the transmitter empty indicator. It is set to 1 whenever the transmitter holding register and the transmitter shift register are both empty. It is at 0 whenever either register contains a byte of data.

Bit 7

Unused and always at logic 0.

Modem status

The modem status register enables handshake and other inputs to be read. The bit functions are as follows:

Bit 0

This is the delta clear to send input. When set to 1 it indicates that the clear to send input has changed state since it was last read.

Bit 1

Similar to Bit 0, but for the data set ready handshake input.

Bit 2

The trailing edge ring indicator detector. It indicates that the ring indicator input has changed from the active state to the inactive state.

Bit 3

This bit indicates that the data carrier detect input of the serial chip has changed state.

Note that bits 0 to 3 generate a modem status interrupt when they are set to 1.

Bit 4

Reads clear to send line.

Bit 5

Reads data set ready line.

Bit 6

Reads ring indicator line.

Bit 7

Reads data carrier detect line.

An easy way to start experimenting with direct control of a serial port is to first set the divisor latch access bit to 1 by writing a value of 128 (decimal) to the line control register. This gives access to the divisor latches so that you can set the required baud rate. Use values of 0 and 12 (decimal) for the most and least significant bytes respectively, which gives a baud rate of 9600. Set the registers back to normal operation by writing a value of 0 to the line control register.

Bytes for transmission are then written to the transmitter register at the base address, but where necessary use a timing loop to prevent bytes from being transmitted at more than one byte per millisecond. Alternatively, use a loop to monitor bit 5 of the line status register. A new byte of data should only be written to the serial port when this bit is at logic 1.

Received data is read from the base address of the port, but this address should only be read when fresh data is available. Whether or not new data is available can be determined by monitoring bit 0 of the line status register. This bit goes to logic 1 when a fresh byte is available, and therefore data should only be read when this bit is at 1. It is automatically reset when the received data register is read. Initially it is probably best not to use interrupts, and to disable interrupts generated by the port so that there are no conflicts with the operating system. This is achieved by writing a value of zero to the interrupt enable register.

Adding a serial port

Most PCs are equipped with two serial ports as standard, so it is not normally necessary to fit additional serial ports. If your PC has a mouse on one serial port and another device such as a modem on the other, there will be alternatives to adding another serial port. Switching to a PS/2 mouse is likely to be the cheapest option, assuming the PC is equipped with a suitable port. A PS/2 mouse port seems to be one of the standard ports these days, so there should be no problem here. Changing to an internal modem is another possibility. Modem cards can be obtained at surprisingly low prices these days. Another option is to obtain a USB to serial adapter so that the modem or other device can be operated via a USB port.

If you do need to add an extra serial port, suitable expansion cards are produced. As with parallel port cards, where possible it is better to use an ISA card. This gives a "proper" serial port at one of the input/output addresses normally used with serial ports. A port of this type can be used in exactly the same way as the built-in ports. A PCI version can only be accessed directly if it is supplied with re-mapping software that intercepts instructions sent to the empty input/output addresses, and replaces them with appropriate routines.

Any reasonably recent printer port card should be capable of at least basic bidirectional operation, but this feature is unlikely to be available if you "dig up" an old printer port card or multi port card. Where available, the input mode is set in exactly the same way as for a built-in port. In other words, set bit 5 of the handshake output register to logic 1. It is usually possible to alter the port's base address and IRQ setting. These settings are usually adjusted via configuration switches or jumpers on the expansion card. The card should be supplied with an instruction manual or an instruction sheet that gives details of the available options.

Four address ranges are set aside for serial ports, so adding one or two extra ports should not give any problems in this respect. You simply have to ensure that the address range of the expansion card is different to the ones used by the built-in serial ports. The Windows System Information utility can be used to check the addresses used by the built-in serial ports. The card should permit its address range to be set at one that will not conflict with the built-in ports. However, if necessary, it should be possible to alter the address ranges of the built-in ports using the BIOS Setup program.

Interrupt request (IRQ) lines are a different matter, since spare IRQ numbers are in short supply on the average PC. In order to avoid conflicts with the existing hardware it is best if the card is not set to use interrupts at all. Unless you actually intend to use interrupts there is no point in having them enabled. With interrupts enabled on the serial port card it is quite likely that conflicts will occur, with the mouse or other hardware ceasing to work properly.

Points to remember

An ordinary serial interface is not suitable for applications that require high transfer rates. The highest standard baud rate of 19,200 transfers data at less than 2 kilobytes per second. Even taking the port to its highest rate of 115,000 baud, data can only be transferred at about 11 kilobytes per second.

A serial interface is a two-way type, enabling eight bits of data to be sent from the PC to a peripheral, or read from a peripheral. Full duplex operation is possible. In other words, data can be sent and received simultaneously.

Many serial interface chips are designed for use with microprocessors, and are not suitable for use in simple add-on devices based on TTL chips. A UART such as the 6402 can be set to the correct word format by hard-wiring its control inputs to the appropriate logic levels. A very basic control logic circuit is all that is required.

The baud rate of a UART is controlled using a crystal oscillator that ensures accurate and consistent results. It is best to use a fairly high baud rate so that relatively fast data transfers are obtained.

The signal voltages used for RS232C interfacing are nominally ±12 volts. UARTs and other serial chips must be interfaced to RS232C signals via line drivers and receivers that provide the necessary voltage shifting. Line receivers and drivers both provide an inversion. Consequently, +12 volts represents logic 0 and –12 volts represents logic 1.

It should not be necessary to use handshaking with your serial add-on circuits. The relatively low speed of serial interfacing means that there is little risk of the PC or the add-on device being fed with data at an excessive rate.

Make sure that the PC's serial port is set for operation without handshaking. It might otherwise refuse to output data because it is not receiving the correct handshake signal. The port's settings are controlled via its properties window, which can be accessed via Device Manager.

Having two types of serial device (DTE and DCE) complicates normal serial interfacing. Due to the lack of any form of handshaking, this should not produce any problems with your own add-on circuits.

Most programming languages have some instructions for dealing with serial communications. However, for the byte by byte communications needed with most add-on circuits it is easier to directly control the PC's serial port hardware. Directly controlling a serial port largely overrides the Windows settings for the port.

Game port
interfacing

Joystick port

Most PCs seem to be supplied complete with a "games" port, which is
usually part of the computer's sound system. It will therefore be on the
soundcard if the computer has one, or on the motherboard with the audio
connectors if the computer has an integrated sound system. It is primarily
intended for use joysticks of the type that contain two potentiometers,
and not switch type joysticks. With the latter the user can only indicate
that an on-screen object should move in a particular direction (up, down,
left, right, or a combination of two adjacent directions).

With a potentiometer style joystick the user indicates a particular screen
position for the controlled object. There are two potentiometers in the
joystick, which provide X (horizontal) and Y (vertical) positions. From
the general interfacing point of view an input port intended for use with
potentiometer joysticks is normally of more value than one intended for
use with switch potentiometers. An input port that can read the settings
of potentiometers is an analogue type that, on the face of it, has numerous
practical applications.

Unfortunately, the "games" port of a PC is a rather basic form of analogue
port. It does not really compare to (say) the 12-bit voltage reading port
of the old BBC Model B machines. It is actually more akin to the "paddle"
inputs on the old Commodore/Atari type joystick port. It responds directly
to the resistance of the potentiometer, rather than having the
potentiometer's track connected across the supply lines and then reading
the wiper voltage. The general scheme of things seems to be to have
the potentiometer in a simple C - R timing circuit. At the beginning of a
timing cycle a software routine starts counting upwards from zero. When
the charge voltage on the capacitor reaches a certain value a "flag" in
the interface changes state, and indicates to the software routine that

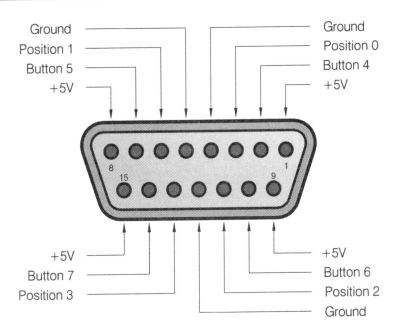

Fig.5.1 Connection details for a PC game port

the count must be halted. The higher the resistance of the potentiometer, the longer it takes for the charge voltage to be reached and the higher the count produced by the software routine.

In theory it is possible to obtain a high degree of linearity with this system. In practice it usually seems to provide quite poor linearity, and is not usually up to the task of accurate measurement. As implemented in a typical PC "games" port there is a definite lack of linearity. Of course, this non-linearity is not important in the port's intended application, but it renders it of relatively little value as a general-purpose analogue port.

There is a further problem in that the port reads resistance rather than voltage, but most signal sources will provide a varying voltage not a varying resistance. This makes it necessary to read most sensors via a voltage-to-resistance circuit, which is a difficult form of conversion, and one that is likely to further impair the linearity of the system. Consequently, the analogue inputs of the games port are not really suitable for precise measurement, but they can be used in non-demanding applications to read sensors such as thermistors and cadmium sulphide photocells.

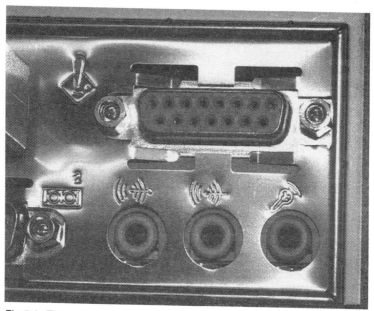

Fig.5.2 The game port connector is a 15-way female D type

The PC joystick ports do not only have analogue inputs, and there are also some digital inputs. These are included as a means of reading the "fire-buttons" of the joysticks, but they are usable as general-purpose digital inputs. With its simple analogue inputs, limited number of digital inputs, and no digital outputs at all, the analogue port is clearly of comparatively limited value as a general purpose port. It can still be useful for a few applications though, and it is worthwhile familiarising yourself with the basics of this port.

Connections

Connection details for the PC "games" port are provided in Figure 5.1. The connector on the computer is a female 15-way D type (Figure 5.2), and you therefore need a male 15-way D connector to make connections to this port. As pointed out previously, it is primarily intended for use with two joysticks of the potentiometer variety. However, there are various types of games controller that use the port's inputs in a variety of ways. This demonstrates the point that it is actually rather more versatile than it

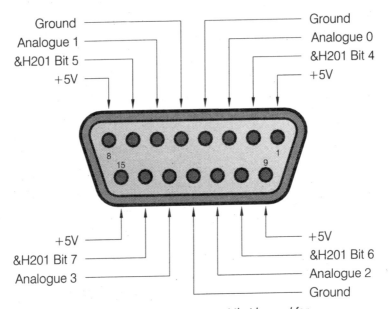

Ground —————————————— Ground
Analogue 1 ————————————— Analogue 0
&H201 Bit 5 ———————————— &H201 Bit 4
+5V ———————————————————— +5V

+5V ———————————————————— +5V
&H201 Bit 7 ———————————— &H201 Bit 6
Analogue 3 ————————————— Analogue 2
Ground

Fig.5.3 Connection details for a game port that is used for general interfacing

is normally given credit for. In the normal scheme of things the "Position" inputs read the settings of the potentiometers, and two of these are needed per joystick (one to provide the X co-ordinate, and the other to provide the Y co-ordinate). The "Button" inputs read the "firebuttons", and there are two of these per joystick.

When using the joystick port as a general-purpose interface it is better to think in terms of the pin identifications shown in Figure 5.3. The inputs that read the potentiometers are a form of analogue input, but they operate in a relatively crude fashion. As explained previously, they directly read the resistance of the potentiometers, rather than reading their wiper voltages. Do not bother trying to get them to directly read voltages, as this is not possible, and could conceivably damage the hardware. For their intended purpose the analogue inputs function well enough, but because they read resistance not voltage, and the degree of linearity provided is very poor, they are of relatively little value for general analogue interfacing.

Figure 5.4 shows the correct method of connection for the joystick potentiometers. Each one simply connects between its analogue input

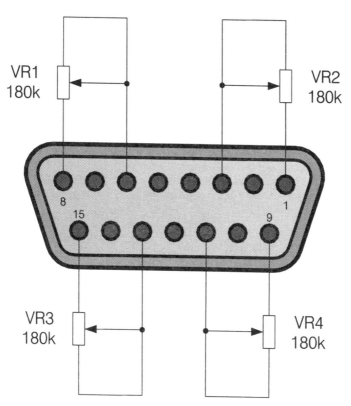

Fig.5.4 Using potentiometers with the analogue inputs

and one of the port's +5 volt supply terminals. The returned value from
each potentiometer seems to be roughly one per kilohm of resistance.
However, as already pointed out the linearity is far from good, and this
can only be used as a very rough guide. Also, on high readings there
seems to be a problem with noise, or there may be some other cause of
the port's erratic operation. Whatever the cause, the port is effectively
rendered unusable with resistances of more than about 180k, and 150k
is a safer maximum resistance value. PC joysticks often seem to use
220k potentiometers in parallel with preset resistors, with the latter being
adjusted to limit the maximum resistance of each pair to about 150k or
so.

Reading

The "firebutton" inputs can be read using the built-in functions of many high level languages, including GW BASIC and Q BASIC. However, when using the joystick port for general interfacing it is probably better if these inputs are read directly. When using GW BASIC or Q BASIC this is achieved using the INP function, and the four "firebutton" inputs are at bits four to seven of address &H201. This is address 513 in normal decimal numbering. You have to read all four bits at once, plus the four unused bits of that address as well. It is a simple matter to mask off any unwanted bits though, so that you can effectively read only the bit or bits that are of interest to you. This is achieved using "bitwise" ANDing. This process has been used in the software featured in earlier chapters, and it is described in detail in the next chapter.

Analogue reading

Reading the analogue inputs directly is probably not worthwhile, and it is much easier to exploit the built-in joystick reading functions of most high level PC languages. When using GW BASIC (or a compatible BASIC) it is the STICK function that is used to read the port. The STICK(0) function returns a value from channel 0 (i.e. analogue input 0), and it also results in readings being taken on the other three channels. These additional readings are stored in memory and can then be returned using the STICK(1), STICK(2), and STICK(3) functions. These read analogue inputs one to three respectively. The important point to note here is that analogue inputs one to three can only be read if a "dummy" reading is first taken from analogue input 0. For example, these two lines of GW BASIC would read analogue input two and print the returned value on-screen.

```
10 DUMMY = STICK(0)
20 PRINT STICK(2)
```

The first line reads analogue input 0 and places the returned value in the variable called "DUMMY". Nothing is actually done with this variable, and the purpose of this line is to take readings on the other analogue inputs, including input two. The second line then reads analogue input two and prints the returned value on the screen. It would seem sensible to use input 0 if only a single analogue input is needed, as this avoids having to continually take dummy readings from this input so that one of

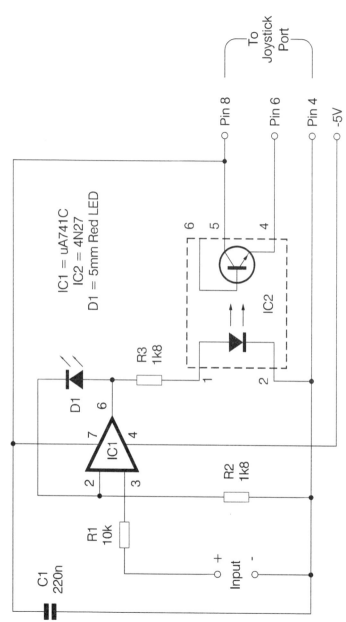

IC1 = uA741C
IC2 = 4N27
D1 = 5mm Red LED

Fig.5.5 The circuit diagram for a voltage to resistance converter

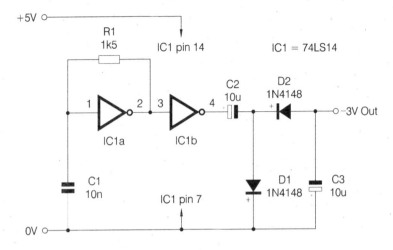

Fig.5.6 A simple negative supply generator

the others can be read. For the same reason, if two or three inputs are needed it would be advisable to ensure that analogue input 0 is one of them.

PCI compatibility

There should be no problem in directly accessing the game port if it is part of an ISA expansion card or it is included with the PC's integrated audio system. There could well be problems if the port is part of a PCI expansion card. This is the usual problem of the PCI card interfacing the port to the processor's busses in an indirect fashion. This makes it impossible to have the hardware directly accessible at the normal input/ output addresses. A port of this type will certainly be "invisible" to a programming language running under MS-DOS.

Under the right circumstances the port might be usable under Windows, where the drivers for the port will provide a means of accessing it. There is no harm in trying to use a games port on a PCI card with your add-ons, but there is no guarantee of success. Getting the port to operate with your add-ons might not be worth the effort if you are ultimately successful. Life will be much easier using a traditional game port on an ISA audio card or fitted on the motherboard.

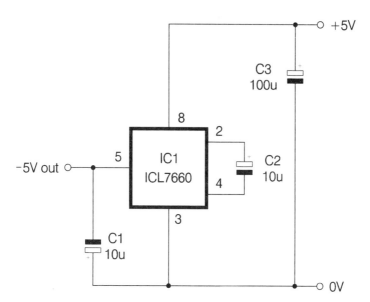

Fig.5.7 The circuit diagram for a more efficient negative supply generator, based on the ICL7660 or equivalent

V to R conversion

Some signal sources can be read directly by the analogue inputs, but in most cases a voltage-to-resistance conversion will be needed. I have experimented with various circuits of this type over the years, and most failed to provide usable results. Of the sundry methods tried, the only simple circuits that gave reasonable results were the ones based on opto-isolators. Figure 5.5 shows the circuit for a voltage-to-resistance converter of this type. The problem in using an opto-isolator is that the LED at its input has an unhelpful forward conduction characteristic. Virtually no current flows until a forward potential of almost two volts is reached, after which only a small increase in voltage is sufficient to produce a large current flow. Adding a resistor in series with the LED gives a better voltage/current characteristic above the two-volt threshold, but still leaves the problem of the threshold itself.

In this circuit non-linear feedback via LED D1 is used to introduce distortion that counteracts the forward threshold voltage in the opto-isolator's LED. This gives a much improved relationship between the input voltage and the reading from the analogue port, but do not expect good linearity. However sophisticated the voltage-to-resistance converter, the basic lack of linearity in the analogue inputs themselves precludes their use in any application that requires absolute measurement. They are only suitable for use where relative measurement is required and a high degree of stability and precision is unimportant.

I used a 5 millimetre RED LED for D1, but practically any LED should give satisfactory results. IC2 can be any "bog standard" opto-isolator, such as a 4N27 or a TIL111. It does not need to be a high efficiency type. In fact it is not a good idea to use a high efficiency device, as this would result in a very low full-scale voltage. Using a low efficiency opto-isolator the full-scale potential is typically about one to three volts. Note that increased input voltage results in decreased values from the analogue input. This could be corrected electronically using an inverter stage ahead of IC1, but it is easier if the software is simply written to take this factor into account.

The circuit of Figure 5.5 requires a –5-volt supply. A simple negative supply circuit such as the one shown in Figure 5.6 can supply this. The circuit consists of a simple oscillator based on two inverting triggers from a 74LS14. The oscillator drives a simple rectifier and smoothing circuit that produces what is likely to be a loaded output potential of about –3 volts. However, this is just about adequate for the negative supply in this case. The circuit of Figure 5.7 is a more reliable way of providing the negative supply, but the ICL7660 and its numerous equivalents are relatively expensive. This circuit provides an unloaded supply voltage that is quite close to –5 volts, but the output potential reduces slightly under loading. The electronic switches in the ICL7660 provide a source resistance of about 100 ohms, so the milliamp or two of supply current drawn by the µA741C operational amplifier will result in minimal loading of the negative supply.

An alternative to providing a negative supply is to use the single supply version of the circuit, which is shown in Figure 5.8. The operational amplifier used must be a type that is capable of single supply DC operation, in addition to operation on a supply potential as low as ±5 volts. Most of the popular operational amplifiers (LF351N, µA741C, etc.) will not work in this circuit.

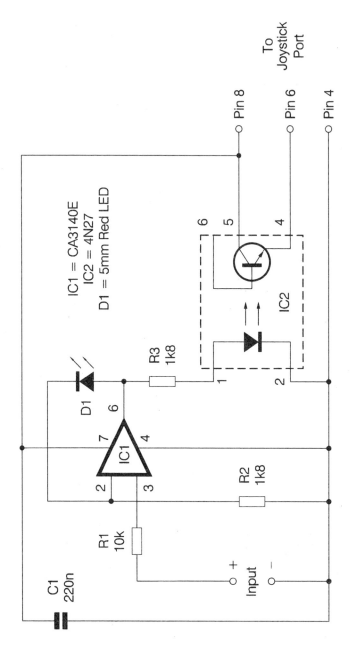

Fig.5.8 A single supply voltage to resistance converter

MIDI port

MIDI (musical instruments digital interface) enables electronic instruments such as synthesisers and sound samplers to be connected together to form a complex music making system. The standard connector for a MIDI interface is a five-way (180-degree) DIN type. The MIDI standard also allows for the use of XLR connectors, which are a high-grade professional type. However, manufacturers of MIDI equipment that use XLR connectors must make suitable adapters available, so that their equipment can be used with standard (DIN type) MIDI leads. Predictably, apart from a few upmarket MIDI expansion cards, PC MIDI ports do not use DIN or XLR connectors. Instead, the game port doubles-up as a MIDI port. A special MIDI cable or adapter is therefore needed to connect a PC to MIDI devices.

Note that the soundcard does not produce any sound via the MIDI port. In the early days of MIDI it was not unknown for uninformed users to connect the output of a MIDI port to the input of an audio system. All this produced was some "clicks" and general noise from the loudspeakers. MIDI is a form of digital interface that has similarities to an RS232C port. It operates on the basis of sending coded messages that carry information such as switch on a certain note with the specified loudness, or switch off a certain note. A synthesiser or other MIDI equipped musical instrument is needed in order to turn these messages into music.

As pointed out previously, normal MIDI cables can only be used with a PC MIDI port via a special cable, which is really an adapter rather than a simple cable. These do not seem to be as readily available as most other PC leads, but they are produced. Your chances of success are probably better with one of the large retailers of electronic musical instruments rather than a computer store. On the face of it, there is no difficulty in making your own leads provided you are reasonably competent with a small soldering iron. Figure 5.9 shows the pin functions for the 15-way D connector when it is used as a MIDI port.

Missing hardware

In reality there is problem in that the soundcard does not include all the hardware for a MIDI interface. The main omission is that the opto-isolator on the MIDI input is missing. It is part of the MIDI hardware standard that all inputs include this isolation circuit. The basic idea is to have the coupling made via light rather than a direct electrical connection. This has each unit in the system electrically isolated from the others, which

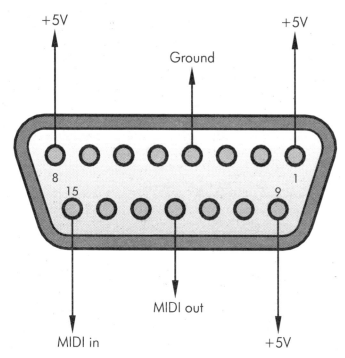

Fig.5.9 Connection details for the game port when it is used in its MIDI role

can help to avoid problems with "hum" loops and digital "noise" entering the audio circuits of the system.

There can also be problems if some units in the system are not earthed, but instead use double-insulation to guard against electric shocks. It is possible to have large voltage differences between the chassis of different units when using equipment of this type. Although the current available is strictly limited, the high voltages are still capable of zapping some of the semiconductors when two units are wired together. Opto-isolation keeps the high voltages at bay and prevents any damage from occurring.

If you buy a PC MIDI lead or adapter, it should include the opto-isolator at the input. There could certainly be problems in using a lead or adapter that lacks this feature.

An opto-isolator is needed at inputs but not at outputs. If you only require a lead to connect the game port's MIDI output to a MIDI instrument, it is

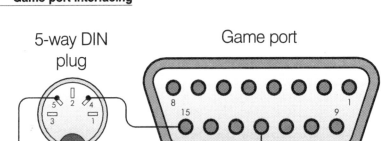

Fig.5.10 *Using the game port as a MIDI output*

not difficult to make your own lead. The two connections required are shown in Figure 5.10. Strictly speaking, the 220-ohm resistor should always be included. In practice the lead will work perfectly well without it, and this resistor is often omitted. Probably the best cable for MIDI use is a good quality twin screened type intended for audio use. The screen should be earthed to the metal shell of the 15-way D connector, but it must not be connected to the 5-way DIN plug.

MIDI input

Matters are not quite as simple if you wish to make your own MIDI input port, but the MIDI input hardware is still very simple. An opto-isolator is required, but few other components are needed. The circuit diagram for a MIDI input port is shown in Figure 5.11. This circuit also has an optional MIDI Thru output, and it is well worth including this feature. It adds to the usefulness of the interface and requires few additional parts. A Thru socket simply retransmits any signals received on the MIDI input, enabling the signals to be coupled to other MIDI devices. Many PC based sequencers have a facility that permits the MIDI output to operate as a Thru socket, but having a genuine Thru output gives greater versatility.

On the input side of the opto-isolator (IC1), R1 provides current limiting in conjunction with a resistor or resistors in the device driving this input. D1 protects the infrared LED at the input of IC1 from high reverse voltages. This is probably not strictly necessary, but it seems to be a standard feature of MIDI input circuitry. Note that no connections are made to

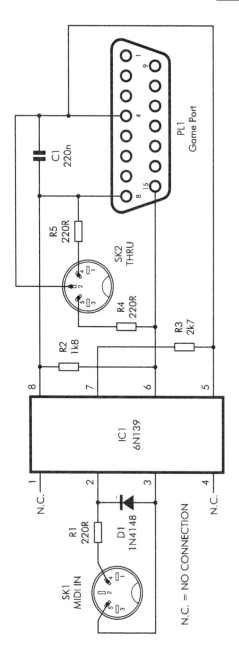

Fig.5.11 A circuit that provides a MIDI input and a Thru output

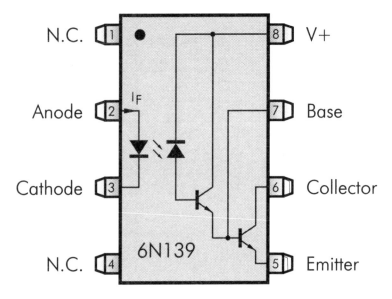

Fig.5.12 Pinout details and internal circuit for the 6N139

pins 1 and 4 of IC1, and these pins are not connected to anything internally either.

The MIDI drive current is just five milliamps, and this necessitates the use of a high efficiency opto-isolator. Although the MIDI baud rate of 31,250 baud is not fast by general electronic standards, opto-isolators are very slow devices. A "bog standard" type can not handle pulse signals at the speeds involved in this application. The opto-isolator must therefore have both good efficiency and higher than normal operating speed. The 6N139 is a good choice because is more than adequate in both respects. Figure 5.12 shows pinout details for this device, together with its internal circuit.

On the input side it has the usual infrared LED. The light sensor on the output side is a photo-diode, and this gives excellent speed. On the other hand, it gives extremely low efficiency, and an amplifier is needed in order to obtain worthwhile performance. This amplifier consists of an emitter follower buffer stage driving a simple common emitter output stage. The latter has an open collector output. This type of amplifier gives excellent gain and a wide bandwidth. The efficiency of the 6N139 is more than adequate for this application and it can handle baud rates something like 10 times higher than the rate used for MIDI links. Note that the 6N139 is not a darlington type. Superficially the two-transistor amplifier of the 6N139 looks similar to a darlington pair, but it is not the same. Darlington opto-isolators have good efficiency, but are extremely slow in operation. They are certainly far too slow for use in MIDI links and will not work in this circuit.

Resistor R3 is the load resistor for the emitter follower buffer stage, and it ensures that this stage operates at a reasonably high current. This in turn ensures that the circuit has a high switching speed. R2 is the collector load for the common emitter output transistor. If the MIDI Thru socket is included, the opto-isolator driven from this output also forms part of the collector load for IC1's output transistor. IC1 can provide enough output current to drive a Thru output and the MIDI input of the PC's game port.

R4 and R5, together with a resistor in the MIDI input circuit driven from SK2, limit the output current to the appropriate level of about five milliamps. The circuit is powered from one of the +5-volt supply terminals of the game port, and the average current consumption is unlikely to be much more than a milliamp. Both transistors in IC1 are switched off under standby conditions, and the circuit only draws a significant supply current during the periods when the input LED is switched on. C1 is a supply decoupling capacitor.

Testing

The interface is very simple, and if it fails to work it is unlikely that the problem lies in the hardware. Problems with MIDI interfaces are more usually due to the port not being set up correctly in Windows. Soundcards tend to cause a certain amount of confusion due to the number of device drivers that are usually associated with them. MIDI usually contributes at least its fair share of drivers, and most soundcards have two or three of these. One of the drivers is for the MIDI port, and it will produce a Roland MPU-401 compatible port. This driver enables the PC to communicate with MIDI synthesisers, keyboards, etc., via the MIDI port, and this one must be installed if you are using the MIDI port.

Confusion often occurs because there are usually other MIDI device drivers. Even the most simple of modern soundcards have some form of built-in sound synthesis, and some cards offer two or three different types. These enable the soundcard to mimic a MIDI synthesiser so that it can be used to play MIDI files. The default MIDI device is normally one of the card's sound synthesisers rather than the MIDI port. The MIDI port might be used in addition to the sound synthesiser, and it should

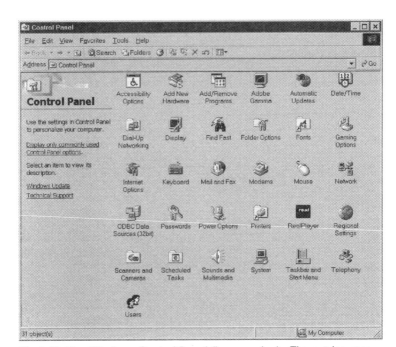

Fig.5.13 The Windows Control Panel (icon version). The entries vary somewhat, depending on the hardware installed in the PC

then be possible to use MIDI software with external MIDI equipment via the MIDI port. If the MIDI port is not used in addition to the built-in sound synthesis, there will be no response from devices connected to the MIDI port.

In order to check the MIDI settings, first launch the Windows Control Panel by selecting Settings and Control Panel from the Start Menu. The Control Panel should look something like Figure 5.13, but depending on the View settings, there might be text entries rather than icons. Either way, there should be an entry called Sounds and Multimedia, and double clicking this entry will produce a window like the one in Figure 5.14. The Sounds and Multimedia Properties window will probably default to the Sounds section. It is the Audio section that is needed in this case, so operate the Audio tab to change the window to one like Figure 5.15.

MPU-401

Activate the MIDI Music Playback menu near the bottom of the window to reveal the available options. In the example of Figure 5.15 there are just two, which are a form of sound synthesis and MPU-401. The available options, and to some extent the terminology used, might vary somewhat depending on the sound system concerned. The MIDI port is unlikely

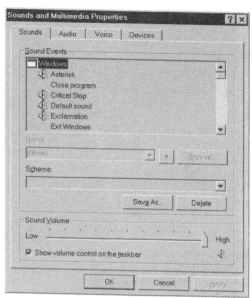

Fig.5.14 The Sounds section of the properties window

to be described as such, and usually includes the MPU-401 name instead. This is because the MIDI port of a PC soundcard or integrated audio system is compatible with the Roland MPU-401 interface, but some are more compatible than others are.

The genuine Roland MPU-401 is a sophisticated piece of electronics that provides more than just some simple port hardware. It contains so-called "intelligence" that takes some of the workload off the PC's microprocessor. This was very useful in the days when PCs were relatively slow and needed all the help they could get from the other hardware. This sort of thing is less important these days, because most PCs have an excess of computing power when used in many applications. In fact the built-in facilities of an MPU-401 interface could actually slow things down when applied to a modern PC.

A MIDI port that has full MPU-401 compatibility will include the built-in intelligence, and should be usable with any applications software that works properly with the real thing. The MIDI ports of soundcards and integrated audio systems have the basic MPU-401 port hardware but almost invariably lack the built-in "intelligence". These are sometimes

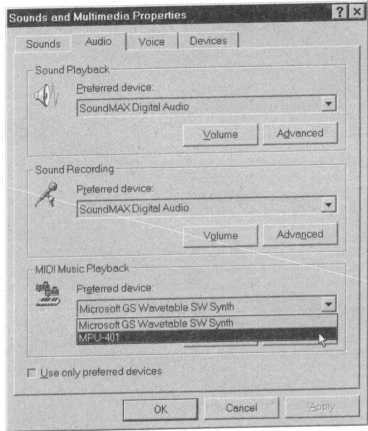

Fig.5.15 The Audio section enables the MIDI output device to be selected

called "dumb" MIDI ports. This lack of full compatibility is not really a major drawback, since most modern MIDI software only uses the basic hardware, or perhaps has the option of using either a full MPU-401 interface or a "dumb" type. Some soundcard device drivers provide a software emulation of the built-in "intelligence". This method should work well enough provided you are using a reasonably powerful PC.

Where appropriate, it is clearly necessary to set the software for use with a basic MIDI port if that is all the soundcard can provide. To be certain that the MIDI output will be used at all, the appropriate option must be selected using the MIDI Music Playback menu. Some music software has built-in facilities for selecting the destination for MIDI output. This facility can only work by overriding some of the Windows sound settings, so check this point if some MIDI software works properly while other software produces no output via the MIDI port.

It can be useful to play a MIDI sequence using the Windows Media Player that is supplied with recent versions of Windows. If a sequence plays properly via an external instrument using this player, but not when using a MIDI program, there is clearly a problem with the set-up of the MIDI program. MIDI applications software usually has a menu that includes a Preferences or Configuration option. Either of these should enable the output of the program to be directed to the MIDI port

Right connections

Probably the most common mistake when wiring up a MIDI system is to connect inputs to inputs, and outputs to outputs. This is unlikely to cause any damage, but will not get the system working properly. The correct method is to connect the MIDI output of the soundcard to the MIDI In socket of the synthesiser. If you need to use a sequencer program to record tracks played on the synthesiser's keyboard, the MIDI Out socket of the synthesiser must be connected to the MIDI input of the soundcard.

Further instruments can be driven from the PC by using the Thru sockets on the instruments and the chain method of connection. In other words, the Thru socket on the first instrument connects the In socket on the next, the Thru socket on that instrument connects to the In socket of the third instrument, and so on.

Tapping off power

Obtaining power for a PC project is not usually difficult if the unit is in the form of an internal expansion card. The ISA expansion ports give access to the supply rails of the PC, and these will normally be sufficient to power your add-on devices. Of course, there is a limit to the amount of power that can be safely tapped off, but there should be no difficulty in tapping off an amp or so from the +5-volt supply. The +12 volt supply can also provide quite hefty currents if required, but note that this supply is not usually well regulated, and it can contain massive amounts of noise. The negative supplies usually have quite modest maximum output current ratings, but it is unlikely that your add-ons will actually need to use them at all.

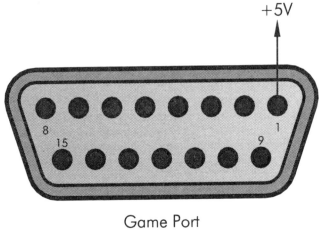

Game Port

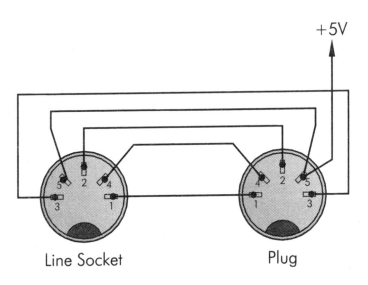

Line Socket   Plug

Fig.5.16 A +5-volt supply can be obtained from the game port or the keyboard port

For an add-on that connects to a serial or parallel port things are somewhat trickier. Neither of these ports have any form of power supply output. If your add-on requires anything other than a straightforward +5-volt supply it is probably best to provide it with its own battery supply or a suitable mains power supply unit. If only a +5-volt supply is needed it is usually better to tap off the supply from one of the PC's ports that does provide a supply output. With most PCs there are two options.

The easiest of these is to take power from the game port. In old PCs a multifunction input/output card generally provides this port. As already explained, in recent models it is usually to be found on the sound card, where it is combined with a MIDI port. With either type of game port it should be possible to obtain a +5 volt supply. The game port connector on the PC is a 15-way female D type, and you therefore need a 15-way male D connector to make the connection to this port. The +5-volt supply can be obtained from pin 1, as in the top drawing of Figure 5.16. Note that many game ports seem to include a resistor or other current limiting circuit on the supply outputs. Consequently, the maximum available current may be just a few milliamps. Higher currents would result in the supply voltage falling to an unusable level.

The usual alternative is to use the keyboard port. There is a slight complication here in that it is necessary to make up a simple adapter in order to enable power to be tapped off while still using the keyboard. Basically all you need is a 5-way 180-degree DIN line socket and a matching plug. The two are wired together as shown in the lower drawing of Figure 5.16, using a short piece of any normal 5-way cable (ribbon, screened, etc.). An additional lead connected to pin 5 of the plug provides the +5-volt supply. The plug connects to the keyboard port of the computer and the keyboard connects to the line socket.

USB power

The same method should be usable with a PC that has a PS/2 style keyboard connector, but it might be difficult to obtain suitable connectors. PCs that have PS/2 mouse and keyboard ports usually have a couple of USB ports as well, and these provide a much easier means of tapping off a +5-volt supply. Each USB port has a +5-volt supply output that can provide up to 500 milliamps (0.5 amps), which is more than adequate for most add-ons. Figure 5.17 shows the usual port arrangement for a PC that has an ATX style motherboard, and it also shows the +5-volt connector on each of the two USB ports.

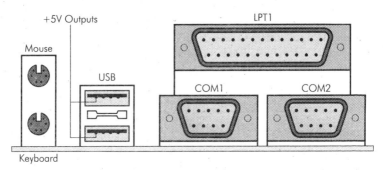

Fig.5.17 If a spare USB port is available, this represents the best way of obtaining a +5-volt supply

If a USB connector proves to be elusive, you can always buy a standard A to B USB lead and cut off the smaller connector. Then strip back the outer sleeving to reveal the individual wires, and do some checking with a test meter to find the wire that carries the +5-volt supply. This wire is then hard wired to your add-on, or the lead can be fitted with a new connector such as a 2.1 millimetre power type. The add-on is then fed with the supply via a matching socket.

Other supplies

In many instances it is possible to design circuits that will work quite happily from nothing more than a +5-volt supply. Occasionally it is impossible to avoid the need for an additional supply. The two simple supply circuits described previously are suitable when a low current supply at about −3 to −5 volts is needed. If a +12 volt supply is needed, it is possible to derive this from the +5-volt supply provided only a modest supply current is required. Figure 5.18 shows the circuit diagram for a suitable step-up regulator, which is based on the LM2577T-12.

The circuit is very efficient (about 80 percent or so), but the step-up process inevitably result in an input current that is much higher than the output current. In fact it is nearly three times higher. Although IC1 can handle currents of up to about three amps, the maximum output current is likely to be dictated by the spare output current available from the +5 volt supply. For example, the maximum output current would only be about 167 milliamps (0.167 amps) with the circuit driven from the supply output of a USB port. Even this figure assumes that no other current was drawn from the supply output of the USB port.

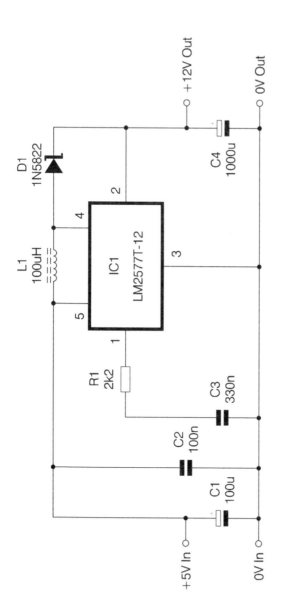

Fig.5.18 A highly efficient 12-volt step-up regulator circuit

Because of the circuit's high efficiency, it should not be necessary to fit IC1 with a heatsink. L1 must be a type that is intended for use in switch mode power supplies, and it must also be capable of handling the maximum output current involved in your application. D1 must have a low forward voltage drop and fast switching speed. Hence a Schottky rectifier has been specified for this component. Any Schottky rectifier having adequate voltage and current ratings should be suitable.

It is not necessary to build your own supply converter, and there are plenty of ready-made DC to DC converter modules available. These permit a +5-volt supply to be stepped up to various voltages, or used to generate negative supply potentials. Battery eliminators are useful if you would prefer to opt for operation on the mains supply. However, bear in mind that the actual output voltage from the non-regulated variety can be almost double the stated voltage under low loading. The "hum" and noise content can also be very high. These supplies will normally be usable only if your add-on includes a suitable voltage regulator circuit. Of course, the regulated type should provide a low-noise output close to the stated output voltage. Battery eliminators can be used in conjunction with DC to DC converts to provide additional output potentials.

Point to remember

The game port has four analogue inputs, but they respond to resistance rather than voltage and have very poor linearity. They are only suitable for the least demanding applications.

It is possible to read voltages using the analogue inputs in conjunction with a voltage-to-resistance converter. However, the poor linearity of the very basic analogue-to-digital converters still precludes their use in anything other than undemanding applications.

There are four digital inputs on the game port, and they can be read using the INP function of GW BASIC or QBASIC, or any similar function. There are no digital outputs on this port.

A game port provided by a PCI card might be of limited use for general interfacing purposes. It will not operate with any MS-DOS programming languages for example, and it is likely to be problematic even when used with Windows programming languages.

If your PC has a spare ISA expansion slot, this can be used to provide a variety of supply voltages. However, it is not a particularly neat way of handling things.

A +5-volt supply can be obtained from the keyboard port or the game port. The maximum current available from the game port is often quite low though. If your PC has a spare USB port, this represents the best way of obtaining a +5-volt supply. A maximum output current of 500 milliamps (0.5 amps) is available from each USB port.

Additional supply potentials can be derived from the +5-volt supply using DC to DC converters. Bear in mind that these circuits are only about 75 to 80 percent efficient. Also, remember that a voltage step-up results in a current step-down. These factors limit the maximum output current that can be obtained using this method.

A modern game port is combined with a MIDI port, but some of the hardware for the MIDI port is missing. A suitable opto-isolator and a few discrete components are needed in order to produce a fully working MIDI interface.

Be careful when using unregulated battery eliminators as the power source. Under low loading the actual output voltage can be nearly double the stated output potential and the noise content on the output can be very high. Supplies of this type need an external regulator circuit for most applications.

Bits and PCs

Low level

Users of high level programming languages are often largely insulated from the fact that computers operate in binary, and that all the data they handle is reduced to a series of 1 and 0s. The software and computer hardware accepts text characters from the keyboard and produces text output on the screen. The situation is very different for those dealing with add-on projects, which usually require control on a bit-by-bit basis. It is possible to design (say) a computer robot that understands the text string "turn left", but most do-it-yourself add-ons are not this sophisticated. The robot is more likely to require something like the binary code 00001111 (0F in hexadecimal). In this chapter we will take a look at the binary and hexadecimal numbering systems, bitwise operations, and how to contact your projects with a high-level programming language.

Applied logic

Some applications are well suited to digital control and it does not take much imagination to see how logic circuits can be put to use in these. As an example, suppose that a circuit must control a row of lights and produce a moving-lights display. Each light is either on or off, and this type of control obviously suits the logic way of doing things with just two signal levels. Each light can be switched on by a logic 1 level and switched of by a logic 0 level. It is just a matter of producing a circuit that will produce the right sequence of 0s and 1s at its outputs, and keep repeating this sequence at the required rate.

Most "real world" applications do not require straightforward on/off switching, but instead deal with quantities of something. For example, a weighing scale does not operate on the basis of something being heavy or not, but deals in actual weights. Digital systems can handle quantities quite easily, and it is just a matter of using a number of digital lines, together with a suitable method of coding. Letters of the alphabet, punctuation marks, etc., are usually represented by ASCII codes, and these use seven lines to carry the codes. Each set of seven 1s and 0s represents a different character. For instance, the code 1010101 represents the upper-case letter "U".

A digital circuit can represent numeric values of any magnitude, but it requires a large number of digits to represent quite modest values. Even so, with the current technology this still represents by far the easiest way of using electronic circuits to handle numbers. Although the mathematics are being handled in what could be regarded as a rather clumsy fashion, the speed of electronic circuits is such that number-crunching is carried out at very high speeds. Also, as already pointed out, the fact that a digital system is operating using 1s and 0s is not normally apparent to the user.

Sampling

Representing a single quantity using logic signals is clearly quite easy, but how does a digital system handle something like an audio signal that is constantly changing? A digital system can handle varying quantities using a system known as sampling. Although this word is now synonymous with digital audio recording, it is in fact a general term that is applicable to any digital system that deals with what is essentially analogue data. It basically just entails taking a series of readings so that the system tracks the rises and falls in the amplitude of the audio signal, temperature, or whatever.

Strictly speaking, a digital system can not fully accommodate analogue signals since it can never have infinite resolution. With analogue signals that are constantly varying, the input signal is converted into a series of fixed values. No matter how frequently samples are taken, there will always be a jump from one sample value to the next. However, provided the resolution of the system is good enough, and samples are taken at a high enough rate, for all practical purposes a digital systems will be as good as an analogue equivalent. The jumps in level from one sample to the next will be of no consequence.

In fact, in many areas of electronics it is now true to say that the best digital systems outperform the best analogue types. Whether a digital system is dealing with individual pieces of data, or a series of samples, the resolution is crucial. In other words, is the jump from one level to the next small enough to enable any value to be depicted with good accuracy? There is no standard resolution that is guaranteed to give adequate results in all applications. The minimum acceptable resolution varies considerably from one application to another.

Bits and bytes

The numbering system we use in everyday life is, of course, the decimal system, or "denary" system as it is alternatively known. This method of numbering is based on the number 10, but it is quite possible to have a system based on any number. There is normally no point in doing so, and the old imperial measures, which were based on a variety of numbers (12 in the case of feet and inches for example), have now been largely phased-out in favour of the metric system.

I suppose that binary could reasonably be regarded as the simplest possible method of numbering. It is based on the number two. In the decimal numbering system the single digit numbers are from 0 to 9, but in binary they are only from 0 to 1. In other words, the only valid numbers for each digit are 0 and 1, and absolutely nothing else is allowed! As already pointed out, representing just two numbers by an electrical signal is very easy. A low voltage is used to represent a 0, and a higher voltage represents a 1. In the case of ports and other external signals these levels are often called "low" and "high" respectively, but these terms are not usually applied to internal signals of a processor. When dealing with internal signals the alternatives of clear (logic 0) and set (logic 1) are often encountered.

Although convenient for the hardware producers, this simple logic system has its limitations and drawbacks. There have been suggestions over the years that circuits which can work directly in decimal will be a practical proposition for widespread use before too long, but there seems to be little real prospect of such a development in the near future. As conventional logic and microprocessor circuits become faster and more sophisticated it becomes more difficult for alternative technologies to compete. For the time being anyway, circuits that work in binary are the only practical ones for general use.

Binary

Binary is easier to understand if you first analyse what an ordinary decimal number represents. If we consider the decimal number 238 for instance, the eight represents eight units (10 to the power of 0), the 3 represents three tens (10 to the power of 1), and the 2 represents two hundreds (10 to the power of 2). Things are similar with a binary number such as 1101. Working from right to left again, the columns of numbers respectively represent the units (2 to the power of 0), the 2s (2 to the power of 1), the 4s (2 to the power of 2), the 8s (2 to the power of 3), and so on. 1101 in binary is therefore equivalent to 13 in decimal (1 + 0 + 4 + 8 = 13).

It takes a lot of binary digits to represent numbers of quite modest magnitude, but this is the price that has to be paid for the convenience of simple binary hardware. A binary digit is normally contracted to the term "bit". One bit on its own is of limited value, and bits are normally used in groups of eight, or multiples of eight. A group of eight bits is normally termed a "byte". A byte can only handle numbers from 0 to 255 (decimal). This is adequate for some purposes, but it is often necessary to handle larger values.

A 16-bit binary number is usually termed a "word", and this gives a range of 0 to 65535 (decimal). 32 bits gives a range of 0 to something over four thousand million, which should be adequate for most purposes. A 32-bit number is sometimes termed a "long word". Modern PCs use 16 or (more usually these days) 32-bit processors, but you will normally do things 8 bits at a time when dealing with user add-ons.

This table shows the number represented by bits in 16-bit numbers, and this might help to clarify the way in which the binary system operates. The numbers in the table are the ones that the bits represent when a 1 is present in that column of the binary number. If there is a 0 in a column, then that column always contributes 0 to the value of the number. We are using the convention of calling the units column bit 0, running through to bit 15 for the left-most column (not bits 1 to 16). The units column is often called the "least significant bit", or "LSB" for short. Bit 31 (or the left-most column that is actually used) is termed the "most significant bit", or just "MSB".

Bit	Decimal Value	Bit	Decimal value
0	1	8	256
1	2	9	512
2	4	10	1024
3	8	11	2048
4	16	12	4096
5	32	13	8192
6	64	14	16384
7	128	15	32768

Signed binary

The binary system described so far, which is often called "direct binary", is inadequate for many practical purposes. It is certainly all that is needed when designing PC based projects, but it is not sufficient for all purposes. The main drawback of direct binary is that it can not handle negative numbers. Obviously you can simply add a minus sign ahead of a binary number to indicate that it is a negative number, but you have to bear in mind that for computer applications this is not valid. There is logic 0 and logic 1, but no logic - level!

The normal way around the problem is to use "signed binary". With a signed binary number the first bit is used to denote whether the number is positive or negative. The convention is for the first bit to be a 0 for positive numbers and a 1 for negative numbers. With this system the normal 8-bit range of 0 to 255 is replaced with a range of –127 to +127 (11111111 to 01111111). The problem is solved at the expense of decreased maximum magnitude for a given number of bits. Note though, that where two or more bytes (or words or long words) are used together to form a large number, only the most significant bit of the most significant byte needs to be used to indicate the sign of the number. It is not necessary to sacrifice the most significant bit of each byte to this task.

Obviously a certain amount of care needs to be exercised when dealing with binary numbers, and you must know whether you are dealing with direct or signed binary numbers. For instance, 10000001 could be 129 (direct binary) or –1 (signed binary). I have encountered computers which have a binary to decimal conversion facility, and which seem to get confused in this way. Results were as expected for answers up to 32767, but things went completely wrong with higher numbers.

This happens where the computer operates with binary numbers of up to 16 bits in length, and it interprets any values that it is fed as signed binary. This works fine if you know that it is working with signed binary. It also works fine if it is fed with binary values of 15 bits in length or less. The leading zeros then inform the computer that the number is a positive one, and the right answer is obtained. For numbers of more than 32767 the most significant bit is a 1, telling the computer that it is a negative number, even if you require a direct binary conversion.

In this basic form the signed binary system has its limitations. The problem is that although it can represent a wide range of positive and negative values perfectly adequately, calculations on simple signed binary numbers do not give the correct result. This is of only academic importance to users of high-level applications programs and applications software. You give the computer such numeric data, positive, negative, or a mixture of the two, and everything is sorted out for you. It is something that is of greater importance to the low-level (assembly language or machine code) programmer, but here we will only consider the high-level approach.

Binary coded decimal

Several microprocessors can operate using another form of binary called "binary coded decimal", or just "BCD", and some computer add-ons require signals in this form. BCD uses four binary bits (often termed a "nibble") to represent each decimal digit. The system operates in the manner shown below.

Decimal number	Binary code
0	0000
1	0001
2	0010
3	0011
4	0100
5	0101
6	0110
7	0111
8	1000
9	1001

The binary number is in fact just the ordinary binary bit code for the number concerned, and it is only for numbers of more than 9 that the system is different. The binary codes from 1010 to 1111 are unused, and all two-digit decimal numbers require 8-bit BCD codes. For instance, the decimal number 64 would be represented by the 8-bit BCD code 01100100. The first four bits (0110) represent the six, and the second four bits (0100) represent the four. Each byte can therefore represent any two-digit decimal number from 0 to 99, which compares to a range of 0 to 255 for an ordinary 8-bit binary number. This helps to contribute to the relative inefficiency of the BCD system.

Of course, when a nibble is incremented by 1 from a value of 1001 (9 in decimal) it does not go to 1010 (which is an illegal code in BCD), but cycles back to 0000. A carry forward of 1 should then be taken to the next BCD nibble. Since the PCs do not operate directly in BCD, you must provide the conversion from direct binary to BCD using suitable software routines. Look-up tables are the normal method for handling this type of thing.

With BCD there is no difficulty in handling large numbers, and it is just a matter of using several bytes in order to accommodate the required number of digits. Negative numbers and decimal points can also be handled with ease by this system, but this requires several additional bits. This information is usually carried in the most significant bits (i.e. the left-hand end of the number), but you can design the software and hardware to handle this type of thing in any way that you see fit. Provided the software and hardware are designed to use the same system everything should work fine.

Hexadecimal

The hexadecimal numbering system is much used in computing. The hexadecimal name is usually abbreviated to just "hex". A problem with binary numbers is that they tend to have many digits with each one being a 0 or a 1, which makes them rather difficult to deal with in many circumstances. For instance, dealing with 10 or 12-bit addresses in their binary form would probably be beyond most peoples' ability, as would dealing with eight-bit data values. On the other hand, binary numbers give a graphic representation of each bit in the register of a microprocessor, control register of a peripheral chip, output terminals of a printer port, or whatever. This is something that is often important, but is especially so when dealing with a microprocessor and its ports.

Decimal numbers are much easier to deal with in that they are much shorter and are in a more familiar form. Unfortunately, a decimal number does not give much idea of the state of each bit in its binary equivalent. Converting a decimal number to its binary equivalent is not a particularly quick or easy process (without the aid of some computerised help anyway). Decimal numbers are consequently rather inconvenient when things must be visualised on a bit by bit basis. Most computer add-ons fall into this category.

The hexadecimal system gives the best of both worlds in that it takes just a few digits to represent even quite large numbers, and it is in fact slightly better than the decimal numbering system in this respect. On the other hand, it is quite easy to convert hexadecimal numbers to their binary equivalents when the state of each bit must be known. The conversion process is quite simple even with very large numbers. The hexadecimal system is based on the number 16, and there are sixteen single-digit numbers.

Obviously the numbers we normally use in the decimal system are inadequate for hexadecimal as there are six too few of them. This problem is overcome by augmenting them with the first six digits of the alphabet (A to F). It is from this that the system derives its name. The table given below helps to explain the way in which the hexadecimal system operates.

Decimal	Hexadecimal	Binary
0	0	0000
1	1	0001
2	2	0010
3	3	0011
4	4	0100
5	5	0101
6	6	0110
7	7	0111
8	8	1000
9	9	1001
10	A	1010
11	B	1011
12	C	1100
13	D	1101
14	E	1110
15	F	1111
16	10	10000
17	11	10001
18	12	10010
163	A3	10100011

What makes hexadecimal so convenient is the ease with which multi-digit numbers can be converted into binary equivalents. The reason for this is that each hexadecimal digit represents four binary bits. Take the hexadecimal number A3 in the above table for example. The digit A represents 1010 in binary, and the digit 3 converts to 0011. A3 therefore represents 10100011 in binary. You may find that you can memorise each of the sixteen four-bit binary codes represented by hexadecimal digits, but a little mental arithmetic is all that is needed in order to make the conversion if you can not.

The digits in a hexadecimal number represent, working from left to right, the number of units, 16s, 256s, 4096s, 65536s, 1048576s, and 268435450s (approx.). In general computing you are unlikely to use hexadecimal numbers of more than eight digits in length, and mostly you will probably only deal with hexadecimal numbers having four digits or less. When dealing with PC add-ons you should not need to use hexadecimal numbers having more than two digits and in most cases you will use only one or two-digit numbers.

Conversions

Conversion from hexadecimal to binary is, as we have already seen, fairly straightforward. With a little experience a little mental arithmetic is all that is needed to make this type of conversion. Conversion in the opposite direction is equally simple. It is just a matter of breaking down the binary number into four-bit groups and then converting each group to its corresponding hexadecimal digit.

Conversions that involve decimal numbers are a little more difficult to deal with. The easy way of handling the problem is to use a computer to make the conversion (or possibly a scientific calculator). Most BASICs can provide a hexadecimal to decimal conversion. If the computer accepts hexadecimal numbers with (say) a "&H" prefix to indicate that they are in hexadecimal, then giving the instruction:

PRINT &HXXXX RETURN

where "XXXX" is the hexadecimal number to be converted, should result in the decimal equivalent being printed on the screen. A conversion in the opposite direction might also be possible, and this is most commonly found in the form of a HEX$ function. You may even find that decimal to octal conversion is possible using an OCT$ function, although these days such a function would seem to be of largely academic interest.

Bitwise operations

In computing numbers are not only manipulated using the normal mathematical functions. There are also the "bitwise" operations called "AND", "OR", and "XOR". These compare two binary numbers (literally) bit-by-bit, and the answer produced depends on the combination of 0s and 1s present in each column. ANDing produces a 1 in the answer only if there is a 1 in that column of both the numbers being ANDed. In other words, if a bit is set to 1 in the first number and the second, a 1 is placed in that bit of the answer. Hence the "AND" name of this logic operation. Here is a simple ANDing example

First number	15	00001111
Second number	243	11110011
Answer	3	00000011

The answers obtained from bitwise operations can tend to look a bit random unless you consider what is happening on a bit by bit basis. A common use of the bitwise AND function is when less than all eight bits of a byte must be read. For instance, assume that we wish to know the state of bit 3 of a register or input port. Most computer systems do not provide any direct means of reading just one bit of a port or register. One way around the problem is to use a bitwise AND operation to mask off the unwanted bits.

In this case bit 3 represents eight when it is set to logic 1, and so the masking number to use is eight (00000100 in binary). In the answer all the bits except bit 3 must be set to zero, as there is no way they can be set to 1 in both numbers. The situation is different for bit 3, where both bits could be at logic 1 if the second number also has this bit set to 1. The answer therefore reflects the state of bit 3 in the second number, and is eight if this bit is high, or zero if it is at logic 0. The ANDing provides the desired function with, in effect, only the required bit being read.

It is possible to read more than one bit if desired. Just set any bits which must be read to logic 1 in the masking number - set any bits which must be masked off to logic 0 in the masking number. As a couple of examples, to read the least significant nibble a masking number of 15 (00001111 in binary) would be used, and to read the most significant nibble the masking number would be 240 (11110000 in binary).

Bitwise OR

Bitwise ORing is a similar process to ANDing, but a 1 is placed in a bit of the answer if there is a 1 in that bit of the first number, or the second number, or both. XORing (exclusive ORing) differs from normal (inclusive) ORing in that it will place a 1 in a bit of the answer if there is a 1 in that bit of the first number or the second, but not if there is a 1 in both bits of these numbers. This could reasonably be regarded as the true OR function, but it has been designated the XOR function. The following example shows how these two types of bitwise operation can produce different answers.

First Number	15	00001111
Second Number	85	01010101
ORed Result	95	01011111
First Number	15	00001111
Second Number	85	01010101
XORed Result	90	01011010

The main use of the bitwise OR function is to permit some bits of a register to be altered without changing the states of the other bits. Suppose that you wish to set bits 0 to 3 of a register to 1. You could simply write a value of 15 (00001111) to the register, but if any of bits 4 to 7 were originally set to 1, this would result in them being changed to zero. The way around this is to read the register, and bitwise OR the result with a suitable value.

Determining this value is quite straightforward. A one is used in the bits that must be set to one, and a zero is used in the other bits. In our example it is bits 0 to 3 that must be set to one, and bits 3 to 7 that must be left unchanged. This gives a masking number of 15. If you look at the bitwise OR example shown previously, where a value of 85 (01010101 in binary) is ORed with 15, you will note that the lower four bits in the answer are all set to one, but the upper four bits remain unchanged. This gives the desired result using just a single instruction.

If you needed to set the lower nibble to zero rather than one, it is a bitwise AND operation that would be used. Use a one in any bits that must be left unaltered, and a zero in bits that must be zero. A value of 240 (11110000) would therefore be used to set the four least significant bits to zero, as shown in this example.

Number In Register	85	01010101
Masking Number	240	11110000
Answer	80	01010000

The bitwise XOR function perhaps has fewer practical uses than the AND and OR functions, when dealing with do-it-yourself add-ons anyway. It is probably the favourite bitwise operation for those involved in graphics. Using an XOR instruction it is possible to complement the bits in a byte (change the 1s to 0s and vice versa) by XORing the byte with 255 (11111111 in binary).

AND in action

A typical application of the bitwise AND function in real world interfacing is when something must not happen until the appropriate bit of an input port goes to the correct state. As a simple example, we will assume that the data lines of the printer port must be read when the Select In handshake line is taken low. This GW BASIC or QBASIC simple routine will do the job:

```
10 REM bitwise AND test
20 CLS
30 OUT &H37A,32
40 SELECT = (INP(&H379) AND 16)
50 IF SELECT = 16 THEN GOTO 40
60 LOCATE 10,10
70 PRINT "          "
80 LOCATE 10,10
90 PRINT INP(&H378)
100 GOTO 40
```

Line 20 clears the screen and then line 30 sets the data lines to act as inputs. The handshake inputs are read at line 40, where the returned value it bitwise ANDed with a value of 16. The Select In handshake line is read at bit 4 of the handshake input register at address &H379, so a value of 16 is used to read this line and mask the other bits. The final value is assigned to the variable called SELECT. This will be set at 16 if the Select In line is high, or 0 if it is low.

The state of the Select In line is checked at line 50. The program loops back to line 40 and tries again if this line is high. It therefore loops around lines 40 and 50 until the Select In line is low, and then the program moves on to line 60. You have to be a little careful with this type of loop, because some programming languages can get stuck with no way out other than the appropriate condition being satisfied. This is not a problem with GW BASIC, where the program can be halted from the keyboard using the normal Control-Break combination. With some programming languages it is necessary to add an instruction or two into the loop in order to provide an "emergency exit".

When the Select In line is taken low and the program moves on to line 60, a LOCATE instruction followed by a PRINT type are used to blank any previous reading on the screen. A further pair of LOCATE and PRINT instructions are then used to relocate the cursor, read the data lines, and print the value on the screen. The program then loops back to line 40 and monitors the Select In line again.

In practice

It is easy to try this routine for yourself. The Select In line drifts high on most printer ports, so the program will probably just loop around lines 50 and 60 when it is run. Connecting the Select In line to ground should result in a reading being taken from the data lines and printed on the screen. This just requires a wire link to be temporarily placed between pins 13 and 25 of the printer port (Figure 6.1). In cases where the Select In line does not drift low there is no major problem. Set one of the handshake outputs high and use this to take the Select In line high. The Strobe output at pin 1 of the port should go high by default, so this provides a convenient means of taking the Select In line high.

If you try the program you will find that it does not work in precisely the required manner. Rather than a reading being taken each time the Select In line is taken low, the program takes a continuous stream of readings whenever this line is low. When dealing with the control logic and program flow it is important to carefully design things so that precisely the required

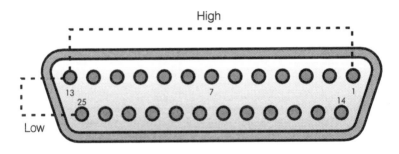

Fig.6.1 The links required to take Select In high or low

action is obtained. It is otherwise inevitable that the system will tend to run out of control or hang up at some point in the proceedings. In this example it is simply running out of control when the Select In line is taken low, and some additional hardware or program code is needed to correct matters.

One solution in this case would be to operate the Select In line via a monostable circuit that provided a very brief low output pulse. A little experimentation is often needed in order to find a suitable pulse length. The pulse must be long enough to be detected reliably by periodic testing of the software loop. On the other hand, it must be short enough to ensure that it does not produce multiple readings. There should be a wide range of pulse durations that give good results.

Another method is to use a second loop to provide a hold off after each reading. This prevents the program from moving into the first loop until the Select In line has returned to the high state. This version of the program includes the second loop:

```
10 REM bitwise AND test
20 CLS
30 OUT &H37A,32
40 SELECT = (INP(&H379) AND 16)
50 IF SELECT = 16 THEN GOTO 40
60 LOCATE 10,10
70 PRINT "        "
80 LOCATE 10,10
```

```
90 PRINT INP(&H378)
100 SELECT = (INP(&H379) AND 16)
110 IF SELECT = 0 THEN GOTO 100
120 GOTO 40
```

The only difference between this program and the original is the addition of a loop routine after the value has been printed on the screen. This prevents the program from returning to line 40 until the Select In line has returned to the high state. The loop at lines 100 and 110 works in exactly the same way as the one at lines 40 and 50, except that a value of 0 is used in the bitwise AND operation. The program therefore loops while the Select In line is high, and exits the loop when it returns to the high state. With the program then looped back to line 40, the first loop is repeated until another pulse takes the Select In line low again. Another reading is then taken and displayed. The program continues in this manner indefinitely with one reading being taken each time that an input pulse is received on the Select In line.

Note that the signal on the Select In line must contain "clean" pulses. On a modern PC it is likely than many thousands of loops per second will be completed while the Select In line is being monitored. Any contact bounce or similar noise on this input will therefore result in a rapid series of readings being taken instead of a single reading. In some applications the spurious readings will be of no practical consequence, but where necessary the input pulses must be "debounced" so that single readings are produced.

Read and write?

Do not make the mistake of assuming that you can ascertain the states of the bits in a write register by reading from that register. Some computer chips do have this facility, but even then the ability to read the register is dependent on the hardware being designed properly. If an address is only used as an output type, reading from it will not produce sensible results. The hardware will not be activated by a read operation, and the data lines will just drift to their natural levels. This often seems to mean that all eight bits go high and a value of 255 is returned.

Another problem is that some input/output addresses have separate functions for reading and writing. In fact it is probable that most input/output addresses fall into this category. Reading from an address then reads from an input port or a status register, rather than producing the last value written to the output port or control register at that address.

Since there are minor differences in the hardware from one PC to another, the fact that reading from a write address works properly on your PC does not mean that it will do so using all PCs.

The safe option is to use a variable to store the value written to a port or control register. This variable must be updated each time a new value is written to the port or control register. You can then determine the value written to each bit by reading the value stored in the variable and applying the standard bitwise AND technique. The sure way of keeping the variable fully up to date is to store new values in the variable, and to then use the variable when writing to the port or register. For example, the two lines shown here could be used to write a value of 127 to the output port or register at address &H301:

```
X = 127
OUT &H301,X
```

If you needed to set bit 4 of a register high without changing the existing states of the other bits, a value stored in the appropriate variable would be bitwise ANDed with a value of 239 (255 − 16). In other words, every bit except bit 4 would be read. A value of 16 would then be added to the answer from the bitwise operation in order to set bit 4 high, giving the final value to be written to the register. For the sake of this example, assume that a value of 85 (01010101) is stored in the variable. This is bitwise ANDed with a masking number of 239 (11101111), giving this result:

Variable	01010101	85
Mask	11101111	239
Answer	01000101	69

Adding 16 to the value of 69 produced by the bitwise AND operation gives this result:

Bitwise result	01000101	69
Value added	00010000	16
Answer	01010101	85

In this example there is no difference between the initial value in the variable and the new value, because bit 4 was already at logic 1. The bitwise AND operation masks bit 4 so that it is set to 0, and the addition sets it high again. The important point to note is that none of the other bits have been altered. If bit 4 had originally been at logic 0, it would have been set to logic 1 by this process, as demonstrated by the next example. Here the initial value in the variable is 170 (10101010)

Variable	10101010	170
Mask	11101111	239
Answer	10101010	170
Bitwise result	10101010	170
Value added	00010000	16
Answer	10111010	186

If you are sure that bit 4 is low, simply adding 16 to the existing value will set it high. Similarly, if you are sure bit 4 is high, deducting 16 from the existing value will set it low. The advantage of the masking and addition method is that it will always give the desired result regardless of the existing state of the bit that is being changed. This eliminates any risk of things getting out of synchronisation, which would scramble the existing bit pattern. Take the example given above, but simply add 16 to the value with bit 4 already high:

Variable	10111010	186
Value added	00010000	16
Answer	11001010	202

Not only is bit 4 at the wrong state in the answer, but some of the other bits have been altered as well. A bitwise AND operation before adding the appropriate value is the safer way of handling things.

The process is simplified somewhat if you need to set one bit to zero without disturbing the others. Having bitwise ANDed the existing value with the appropriate masking number there is little point in adding zero to the value before writing it to the register. Simply perform the bitwise AND operation and then write the resulting value to the control register or output port.

Changing bits

In some cases it is necessary to alter more than one bit while leaving the others unchanged. The same basic process can be used with several bits. Suppose that you wish to set bits 0 to 3 high while leaving the other bits unaltered. In order to mask bits 0 to 3, a binary value of 11110000 is required in the bitwise AND operation. This is equivalent to 240 in decimal numbering. In this example a value of 170 is present in the variable used to store the current value in the register.

Variable	10101010	170
Mask	11110000	240
Answer	10100000	160

Adding 15 to the answer (00001111 in binary) sets bits 0 to 3 high.

Bitwise result	10100000	160
Added value	00001111	15
Result	10101111	175

This has given the desired result, with bits 0 to 3 set high and bits 4 to 7 at their original settings. Again, if you need to set certain bits low, it is only necessary to bitwise AND using the appropriate masking value and then write the result to the port. There is no point in adding zero to the value first. Where it is necessary to set some bits low and some high, start with a bitwise AND operation in the normal way and then add the appropriate value to the answer. For instance, suppose that in the previous example a bit pattern of 1001 rather than 1111 was required in bits 0 to 3, and that the other bits had to be left unaltered. This method would be used:

Variable	10101010	170
Mask	11110000	240
Answer	10100000	160

Adding 1001 to the answer (9 in decimal) sets the right bit pattern in bits 0 to 3.

Bitwise result	10100000	160
Added value	00001001	9
Result	10101001	169

Once again, the required action has been obtained, with the appropriate bit pattern in bits 0 to 3, and bits 4 to 7 left unaltered.

Changing addresses

With small programs it is not difficult to alter the input/output addresses if, for example, you wish to change a program written for printer port 1 to make it work with printer port 2. A ploy often used with longer programs is to place the port addresses in variables near the beginning of the program. I suppose that strictly speaking these are constants rather than variables, since the program does not alter the values that they contain. The idea is to use the variables in INP and OUT instructions in place of the port addresses. Should it become necessary to use different addresses, it is merely necessary to alter the lines where the addresses are assigned to the variables. The new addresses will then be used in INP and OUT instructions via the new values assigned to these variables. This simple program repeatedly reads what will normally be printer port 1 at the base address of &H378 (888 decimal):

```
10 REM Easy to change port addresses
20 PRN1 = &H378
30 PRN2 = &H379
40 PRN3 = &H37A
50 CLS
60 OUT PRN3,32
```

```
70 LOCATE 10,10
80 PRINT "            "
90 LOCATE 10,10
100 PRINT INP(PRN1)
110 GOTO 60
```

Lines 20 to 40 assign the three port addresses to variables called PRN1, PRN2, and PRN3, but in this small program PRN2 is not actually used. The OUT instruction at line 60 uses PRN3 instead of the relevant port address, and PRN1 is used in the INP instruction at line 100. This indirect way of using input/output addresses does not significantly alter the way in which a program operates, and it provides the same action as an equivalent program using the appropriate values in the INP and OUT instructions. In theory it could slow things down slightly, but in practice any reduction in speed is likely to be unnoticeable.

In order to change the program to operate with printer port 2 it is merely necessary to change the values assigned to the three constants, as in this version:

```
10 REM Easy to change port addresses (modified)
20 PRN1 = &H278
30 PRN2 = &H279
40 PRN3 = &H27A
50 CLS
60 OUT PRN3,32
70 LOCATE 10,10
80 PRINT "            "
90 LOCATE 10,10
100 PRINT INP(PRN1)
110 GOTO 60
```

In this example there are only two instructions that use the constants, making their use a pointless exercise. However, these programs demonstrate how this method is used, and with some types of interfacing there are dozens of INP and OUT instructions. Using constants can then save a great deal of time if the port addresses have to be altered. Also, using constants reduces the risk of mistakes being made, and they are easily spotted and rectified if you should slip up.

Address selection

Things can be taken a step further, with the address range being selected before the program starts operating properly. With a gadget that interfaces to a printer port for example, a choice of the three address ranges could be provided when the program is first run. The user then selects the appropriate range and the program goes into its main routine. In this way a single version of the program can accommodate any standard printer port.

This program provides the same basic action as the one described previously, but it enables the user to select the required printer port base address via the keyboard.

```
10 REM Program to set port addresses
20 CLS
30 PRINT "PRESS 1 FOR BASE ADDRESS &H278"
40 PRINT "PRESS 2 FOR BASE ADDRESS &H378"
50 PRINT "PRESS 3 FOR BASE ADDRESS &H3BC"
55 PRINT "AND THEN PRESS RETURN"
60 INPUT A$
70 IF A$ = "1" THEN PRN1 = &H278
80 IF A$ = "2" THEN PRN1 = &H378
90 IF A$ = "3" THEN PRN1 = &H3BC
100 IF A$ = "1" THEN PRN3 = &H27A
110 IF A$ = "2" THEN PRN3 = &H37A
120 IF A$ = "3" THEN PRN3 = &H3BE
130 PRINT PRN1
140 PRINT PRN3
150 OUT PRN3,32
160 LOCATE 15,15
170 PRINT "          "
180 LOCATE 15,15
190 PRINT INP(PRN1)
200 FOR D = 1 TO 20000
210 NEXT D
220 GOTO 160
```

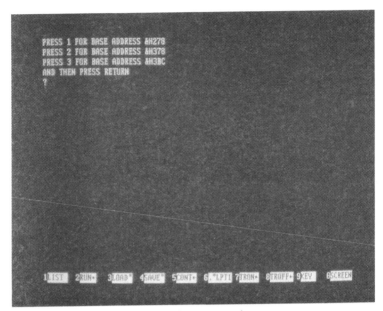

Fig.6.2 The initial screen when the program is run

The program starts by clearing the screen and it then prints four lines of instructions on the screen (Figure 6.2). These indicate that keys 1, 2, and 3 should be pressed to select base addresses of &H278, &H378, and &3BC respectively. The Return key is then operated to actually input the selection. Line 60 is an INPUT statement, and it is this that reads the keyboard. The string typed in here is assigned to the string variable called A$.

A series of IF...THEN instructions test the contents of A$ and set variables PRN1 and PRN3 to the appropriate values. For example, if line 100 detects that A$ contains just the 1 character, it sets PRN3 at a value of &H27A. In a real world application it would probably be necessary to include error trapping in this part of the program. It has not been included in this simple example program, so make sure you only enter 1, 2, or 3 if you try it yourself.

Lines 130 and 140 are not essential, and they simply print the values of PRN1 and PRN3 on the screen so that you can see that the correct port addresses have actually been selected. Note that the values will be printed in decimal form (Figure 6.3), so the base addresses will be given

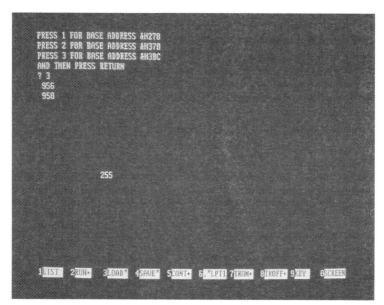

Fig.6.3 The screen once the address range has been selected

as 632, 888, and 956, and the handshake output addresses are 634, 890, and 958. Line 150 sets the data lines of the appropriate printer port as inputs, and it uses the value stored in PRN3 as the output address. The program then goes through the usual loop, which repeatedly reads the data lines and prints the returned values on the screen. The FOR..NEXT loop within the main loop is used to slow things down and produce flicker-free display.

In this example program in GW BASIC the port addresses are set using input from the keyboard. Visual programming languages make it easy to use alternatives such as buttons, radio buttons, and menus to provide address selection. With serial and parallel port add-ons, it is certainly worthwhile equipping programs to handle any of the standard port address ranges.

Points to remember

Unlike an analogue system, a digital type can not represent an infinite number of levels. With an eight-bit system for example, only 256 different levels can be accommodated. There is inevitably some rounding up and down when an analogue signal is digitised, but good results will be obtained provided the resolution of the system is adequate for a given application.

Bear in mind that there is more than one form of binary numbering. Simple binary, signed binary, and binary coded decimal (BCD) are all in common use. You will not get sensible results if one type of binary is processed as if it was of a different type. Odd results are often produced by signed binary values being treated as the simple binary variety, and vice versa.

Hexadecimal numbers are used a great deal in general computing, and are likely to be encountered frequently when undertaking PC interfacing. It is not essential to understand this numbering system, but you will certainly find a knowledge of hexadecimal more than a little useful.

The bitwise AND operation is crucial to most PC interfacing. It enables a certain bit or bits to be read while others are masked. PC programming languages generally lack instructions for reading ports on a bit by bit basis, so the bitwise AND option is usually the only option.

OR and XOR bitwise operations are also available. These have their uses, but are used much less than bitwise AND operations in PC interfacing.

Do not rely on reading an input address to determine the state of bits in an output port or control register. In most cases you will get erroneous results from an input port that is completely separate from the hardware at the output version of the address. In others you will simply be reading from a non-existent port. The safer option is to write the output data to a variable and then to the output address. Reliable data can then be read from the variable.

It is often necessary to alter some bits of a register while leaving others unchanged. This can be accomplished by first using a bitwise AND operation to set to zero the bits that must be altered. Adding the appropriate value then sets these bits at the correct state while leaving the others intact.

With programs that operate in conjunction with hardware on a serial or parallel port, it is advisable to provide an easy mans of changing the input/output address range. The hardware and software should then be usable with any PC that has standard ports.

Windows programming

Windows in and outs?

The generally accepted wisdom is that Windows programming languages do not permit direct accessing of the ports, but this is not totally true. In fact it is far from the truth. It is true many modern Windows programming languages do not include direct port access as a standard feature, including the most popular language of them all, which is Visual BASIC. However, this facility can be added to virtually any Windows programming language via an add-on, plug-in, or whatever. Of course, this is only feasible in practice if you can find a ready-made add-on or can produce one for yourself. Fortunately, there are several add-ons to choose from, and some of them are free.

There are at least a couple of other options available, and one of these is to use Borland's C++ 4.5 to compile a standard MS/DOS C++ program. In the MS/DOS versions of C++ it is usually possible to access the ports using the "inp" and "out" instructions. Borland's C++ 4.5 supports both of these instructions, and will compile MS/DOS C++ programs into Windows programs. In fact you end up with what is still basically the original MS/DOS program, but it runs under Windows in its own Window.

This could be more convenient than running the MS/DOS original via the Windows "MS/DOS Prompt" option or rebooting in MS/DOS mode, but it is not really a big step forward from either of these. Also, you have to bear in mind that the program produced is a 16-bit Windows type. This should work properly if run under Windows 3.1, 95, 98, or ME, but would presumably fail to work with Windows NT or 2000. Full compatibility with Windows XP is also unlikely, and total failure is quite likely.

Borland C++ 4.5 is no longer available, but I believe that it was included with some later versions in order to provide users with a means of producing 16-bit Windows programs. It has also been given away free with some computer magazines, but there are some restrictions on the use of the "free" version. These should not be a problem if you are only using the program for personal use, but any commercial or formal educational use seems to be prohibited. Anyway, if you wish to pursue this approach it might be possible to track down Borland C++ on the Internet. Unless you need to produce 16-bit Windows programs for some reason, I would certainly recommend a different approach.

Delphi

There is a better solution to producing Windows programs for your projects in the form of Delphi, which is another Borland product. Unfortunately, only the original version of Delphi (now usually referred to as Delphi 1) supports direct port access. You may find references to the relevant commands in the on-disc documentation of later versions, but the commands themselves are not implemented. Delphi 1 produces 16-bit Windows programs, but like C++ 4.5 programs, these should run perfectly well under Windows 95, 98 or ME. As far as I am aware, Delphi 1 is no longer available as a separate product, but it was certainly included with some of the later versions to provide a means of producing 16-bit programs. However, it would be as well to check this point before buying version 4 in order to obtain the original Delphi program.

Delphi 1 has also been given away free with some computer magazines, but like the "free" version of C++ 4.5 there are some restrictions on its use. Anyway, a search of the Internet might produce a source for this program, or it should be possible to buy an early version of Delphi at low cost on the second-hand market. Using Delphi is probably not the best method if you are an experienced BASIC programmer, but it is certainly worth a try if you have some experience with Pascal or are new to programming. As explained later in this chapter, the 32-bit versions of Delphi can also be used with your add-ons, albeit in a more roundabout way. If nothing else, Delphi 1 is useful as an easy way of gaining experience before moving on to a later version.

Advantages

So why is Delphi better than using C++ version 4.5, or simply sticking with GW BASIC, etc? Delphi is a "visual" programming language (like Visual BASIC) that makes it easy to produce standard Windows style programs, complete with control buttons, dialogue boxes, scroll-bars, and all the familiar Windows gadgets. There is insufficient space available here for in-depth coverage of Delphi programming, which seems to require a minimum of about 3000 pages! We will only consider the basics of getting Delphi to directly access the ports. In order to produce Delphi programs for most projects you do not need to be an expert in this programming language, so once you have digested a few fundamentals of Delphi programming it should not be too difficult to get your projects operating via a Windows environment.

Visual programming

If you are only familiar with traditional programming languages such as GW BASIC it is only fair to point out that Delphi and other visual languages are a rather different concept. You still have to do some traditional programming with variables, loops, and so on, but much of the code is produced without the need for any programming. Delphi is based on the Pascal programming language, and Object Pascal is the language at the heart of the system. This is apparently based on Borland's Turbo Pascal programming language, which was very popular in its day. Anyone who is familiar with the Pascal programming should have little difficulty in learning to use any version of Delphi.

So just how does visual programming differ from the traditional approach? The differences start to become apparent as soon as Delphi is first run. Unusually, at start-up there are four windows open (Figure 7.1). The window at the top of the screen has the usual menu bar, etc., and could be regarded as the main program window. The majority of the section below the menu bar contains the component palette. This makes it easy to add all manner of objects into your programs, including buttons, pull-down menus, and labels.

What is termed the form is situated below the component palette, and the form is where you design the visual appearance of you finished program. The size of the form determines the starting size of the program window, and if you place a button in the bottom left-hand corner of the form, a button will appear in exactly the same place in the program window. The form has a grid of dots to help you place components accurately, but these are not shown in the program window. You can actually have more than one form per program, but we will settle for just one form in the demonstration programs featured here. One form is normally sufficient.

The Object Inspector occupies the left-hand portion of the screen. This provides control over the form and the components contained within it. You can adjust the size and position of objects by dragging them or by

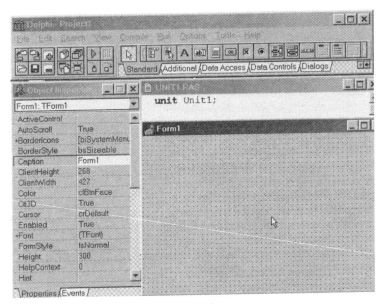

Fig.7.1 At start-up Delphi has four windows open

entering the relevant figures into the Object Inspector. In most cases it is easier to drag objects to the required position and shape. It is only necessary to resort to the Object Inspector when the size and (or) position must be set with great precision. The Object Inspector also provides control over colours, text fonts and sizes, and a great deal else.

Largely hidden behind the form you will find the Code window, which is where the program code is entered. However, with the visual programming method the amount of traditional program writing required is sometimes quite small. A lot of the program code is produced simply by dropping buttons, etc., onto the form and adjusting parameters. The programming language generates the code that produces these objects.

This is not to say that no programming is required. You must enter some code for a button or operating it will have no effect. In advanced applications a great deal of "hand written" code will be required, but the visual approach takes much of the hard work out of Windows programming. It also makes it quick and easy to make changes to the appearance of the program. If a button needs to be moved slightly to the left and made smaller, you just drag it to the left, resize it and recompile the program.

It is only fair to point out that the structure of visual programs is radically different to those produced using traditional programming techniques. If you are used to using an old style programming language such as GW BASIC, you will have to drastically change your ways of thinking in order to properly utilise a visual programming language. The programmer is less concerned with the flow of the program when using a visual programming language. It is still necessary to ensure that the program does not get stuck in loops, end prematurely, etc., but much of the flow is controlled by the programming language.

Visual programs are event driven, and you have to master this concept in order to produce working programs. Most of the time the program will just sit there doing the computer equivalent of twiddling its thumbs, waiting for something to happen that generates an event. An event is often generated by user input such as someone operating a button or selecting a menu item. However, an event can be generated automatically, by a timer timing out perhaps.

Outputting data

Delphi 1 provides access to the ports via the port and portw functions. These are respectively used for eight and 16-bit operations, and here we will only consider eight-bit port accesses. Depending on the syntax used, port can be used to read from a port or write data to it. This program line would write a value of 123 to printer port 1 at address 888 (decimal):

```
Port[888] := 123;
```

Note that the port address is contained in square brackets, and not the ordinary brackets (parentheses) used with the BASIC OUT instruction. Also note that in this context the equals sign must be preceded by a colon, and that all normal Pascal program lines end with a semicolon. As a simple test of writing to a port select the button component in the component palette, and click the mouse at two points on the form. This will drop two buttons onto the form. Select one of these and change its caption to "85". Then double-click on the button to bring up the code window, which will contain the basic framework for your program. Your code for the button goes between the words "begin" and "end", and only this line of code has to be added:

```
Port[888] := 85;
```

Next click on the other button to select it and use the Object Inspector to change its caption to "170". Then double-click on the button and add this program line in the code window between "begin" and "end".

```
Port[888] := 170;
```

You can now save this project and the code, and then select the "Compile" option from the "Compile" menu to produce a stand-alone program file that can be run under Windows 3.1, 95, 98 and ME. This is different to GW BASIC and QBASIC where your programs must be run within the programming language. These are known as interpreted languages. As the programming language encounters each instruction it converts it into the appropriate machine code, and then runs it. Apart from the fact that compiled programs are free to run independently, they are usually very much faster than interpreted programs. The program code has already been interpreted and is ready to run. Interpreting typically takes at least 10 times longer than actually running the code, so compiled programs are massively faster than interpreted equivalents.

Delphi gives the option of trying out the program without compiling to a standalone program first. Simply select "Run" from the "Run" menu and the program will run from within Delphi. Either way you should get a program window the same size as the form, complete with the two captioned buttons. Pressing the "85" button will output the binary code 01010101 to printer port one. Pressing the "170" button outputs the binary code 10101010 to the port. Of course, a variable can be used instead of a number in the Port instruction, but it must be a variable of a suitable type such as a byte or integer variable. Trying to output a variable of an inappropriate type will generate an error message when compiling the program. As explained in the next section, Delphi is less easygoing with variables than are most versions of BASIC.

Reading

Reading a port requires the Port instruction to be used in this form:

```
Variable := Port[Address];
```

Delphi requires variables to be declared before they are used in the program, and they can not simply be made up as you go along. Also, you have to be careful that you only use variables in an appropriate fashion. With BASIC you can read a port and then print the returned value on the screen with a minimum of fuss. With Delphi matters are slightly more difficult because the value read from the port must be placed in an integer or byte variable, but writing text to the screen requires a string variable. This requires a type conversion from a byte or integer to a string variable before the returned value can be printed. In order to set up the byte and string variables these two lines could be added in the Code window under the "var" heading:

```
Reading : Byte;
S : String;
```

This sets "Reading" as a byte variable, and this is the variable that will be used to store the value returned from the port. Variable "S" is a string variable, and this will be used to hold the text converted from "Reading". These program lines could be assigned to a button, and would print the value returned from printer port one each time the button was clicked. Note that this will only work if printer port one is a bidirectional type.

```
Port[890] := 32;
Reading := Port[888];
Str(Reading, S);
Canvas.TextOut (50,50, '        ');
Canvas.TextOut (50,50, S);
```

The first line outputs a value of 32 to the port to set it to the input mode. The next line then reads the port's data register and places the result in the variable called "Reading". The third line takes the value contained in "Reading" and converts it into the corresponding text string, which is placed in variable "S". Line four writes a series of spaces to the form, and this is done to blank any previous reading that is displayed. Finally, the string contain in "S" is printed on the form, 50 pixels down and 50 pixels in from the top left-hand corner of the form. The value on the screen is updated each time the button is clicked.

Time after time

Delphi provides facilities that are potentially very useful when writing software for your add-ons. The next program demonstrates two of these, which are the interval timer component and the graphics facilities. By default the timer executes its section of code every second, but the interval can be altered by the user and has a resolution of one millisecond. The timer component can be found in the component palette but it is not in the "Standard" set shown at start-up. If you click on the "System" tab of the component palette the timer button will be displayed. If you click on this and then click anywhere on the form the timer object will be installed in the form.

This is not a visual component, and the timer icon will not appear in the program window when the program is run. The icon appears on the form to remind you that it is in use, and to provide you with access to its properties. The positioning of the timer is therefore unimportant, and it can be placed anywhere out of the way of other components. Double-click on the timer icon to bring up the code window and then add this code between "begin" and "end":

```
Timer1.Interval := 250;
Canvas.TextOut (55, 0, '0');
Canvas.TextOut (55, 50, '50');
Canvas.TextOut (55, 100, '100');
Canvas.TextOut (55, 150, '150');
Canvas.TextOut (55, 200, '200');
Canvas.TextOut (55, 250, '250');
port[890] := 32;
Reading := port[888];
Form1.Canvas.FillRect (Rect (0, 0, 50, 300));
Form1.Canvas.Pen.Width := 5;
Canvas.MoveTo (25, 0);
Canvas.LineTo (25, Reading);
```

Also, under the "var" heading add this line:

```
Reading : Byte;
```

The purpose of the program is to produce a simple bargraph display that shows the values returned from the printer port, which must be a bidirectional type. The first line of the program sets the timer interval at 250 milliseconds, but you can use any valid value here. Bear in mind

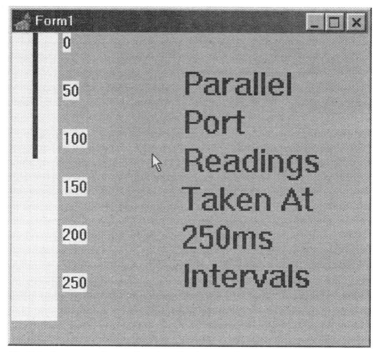

Fig.7.2 A screen dump showing the bargraph program in operation

that the screen only updates at around 50 to 90 times per second, and that there is no point in using very low interval values. A series of six program lines then print a scale of values for the bargraph. Next the port is set to the input mode and then the value read from the port is stored in a variable called "Reading". Then a rectangle is drawn in the default colour (white), and this produces a panel for the bargraph to operate in. It also blanks out the previous reading so that the new one can be displayed properly.

The next three lines actually draw the line of the bargraph. First the pen width is increased from the default value of one pixel to five pixels so that the bargraph is easier to see and read. The MoveTo instruction moves the pen to the specified screen co-ordinates but does not actually draw anything on the screen. Finally, the LineTo instruction actually draws the line, with variable "Reading" defining how far down the screen the line is drawn. If you add a label to describe the function of the program, then compile and run it, you should end up with something along the lines of Figure 7.2.

Eventing

The event driven nature of visual programs was pointed out previously, and even the very simple programs featured here demonstrate this point. The program that uses two buttons to output values to the printer port lacks any normal structure. In the conventional sense, it has no loops or conditional branches. It even lacks a true starting point. When the program starts it produces a window of the appropriate size and design, and then waits for an event. In this example there are only two normal events and operating the buttons generates these. The relevant program code is performed when a button is operated and an event is generated. You do not have to write code to repeatedly check each button to determine whether it has been operated. This is handled by the programming language, which detects all events and proceeds accordingly.

The situation is similar with the port reading program, but it does not rely on user generated events. Instead, an event is generated on each occasion that the timer counts down to zero. This produces a regular stream of events, and readings from the port. The program is in a simple loop, but in this case there is no need for the programmer to bother with loops and timing routines. Delphi and the timer component handle all this. The programmer still has to produce some conventional loops and conditional branches when writing most programs, but the event driven method greatly reduces the need for this type of thing.

You generally start by working out the screen layout and then add the code to make each element of the system work. Most conventional programs are structured as a main routine and a number of subroutines that are called from the main program as and when necessary. Things are not really that much different when using a visual programming language. The main program might not exist as such. Some initial setting up is usually required, and this can be assigned to the form so that it is executed when the form loads. This code forms part of the main program, but most of it is generated by the programming language.

An event is produced if someone clicks a button, but you do not write any code to generate the event. You write the code that makes the right thing happen when an event is generated. Writing this code is much like writing a subroutine for a conventional program, and it is a form of subroutine. Visual programming is sometimes criticised because it enforces a "bits and pieces" programming style, but well structured conventional programming using subroutines is not really that much different.

I am not sure if you can achieve anything using Delphi that could not also be achieved using a conventional BASIC or Pascal programming language, but it is clearly possible to do many things much more easily using a visual language such as Delphi. Things that require no programming using a visual language such as Delphi could easily take hours of programming using conventional methods. Changes to the layout are easily accomplished and simply require objects to be dragged around the form. This type of change can involve hours of work will conventional programming.

The fact Delphi produces stand-alone programs that run under Windows 3.1, 95, 98 or ME make it an attractive proposition for those who are no longer prepared to use MS/DOS, which these days probably means the vast majority of PC users. Although Delphi is not the fastest programming language around, it is a compiled language and on any reasonably modern PC it certainly runs at a rate that is fast enough for the vast majority of applications.

Delphi 2, etc.

Later versions of Delphi lost the Port instruction, but they can still be used to directly access the ports. This is possible due to the inclusion of an inline assembler that makes it easy to add assembly language routines into programs. The assembler does, of course, include standard 80** series instructions that enable the ports to be accessed. This method is not as simple and straightforward as using the Port instruction, but it is not particularly difficult either. The inline assembler is about as easy to use as it could be.

Fortunately, you do not have to be an expert at PC assembly language programming in order to use this method. In fact, you do not need to know anything about assembly language at all. You can use standard routines to read from ports and place the returned values in variables. Everything else can then be handled using normal Delphi programming. Similarly, when writing data to ports it is merely necessary to use a standard assembly language routine to write the data to the port. Everything else can be handled using normal Delphi instructions.

Assembler

It is very easy to use the assembler, and it is just a matter of heading your code with "asm" and finishing with "end". There is one slight complication, which is that you must ensure your assembly language routines do not interfere with the normal running of the computer. What this means in practice is that any changes made to the contents of certain registers must be reversed before the routine is terminated. The simple routine shown here is all that is needed to write to a port.

```
begin
OptVal := ScrollBar1.Position;
asm
push dx
mov dx, 888
mov al, OutVal
out dx, al
pop dx
end;
end;
```

This routine reads the value produced by a scrollbar and outputs it to the data lines of printer port 1. It is assumed here that this is at input/output address 888 (&H378). Where appropriate, the address must be changed to suit the base address of the port you are using. By default, a scrollbar produces value from 0 to 100. In order to use the full range of eight-bit values this must be changed to 0 to 255. This is just a matter of selecting the scrollbar and then altering Max value in the Object Inspector (Figure 7.3). The scrollbar must be made reasonably large if it is to provide a range of 256 different values. OptVal is the variable used to store the reading from the scrollbar. This is a byte-size variable that must be declared in the appropriate part of the program.

The assembly language routine accesses the port using indirect addressing via the dx register. The push instruction stores the current contents of this register on the top of the Stack. A move instruction is then used to place the port address in dx. This is the base address of printer port 1 (888) in this example, but any valid address can be used here. Next another move instruction is used to transfer the value stored in OptVal to the al register, which is the accumulator. Then the out instruction outputs the value stored in accumulator to the address contained in the dx register. Finally, the contents of the dx register are restored from the top of the Stack by the pop instruction. Two end instructions are needed to terminate the routine. The first one terminates the assembly language routine and the second one ends the subroutine as a whole.

16-bit transfers can be achieved by using the ax register instead of the al register. There is actually a direct addressing mode where the port address is supplied in the out instruction. On the face of it this is a more simple method that is better than the indirect method. However, this method only supports eight-bit addresses. As user add-ons are normally at addresses from 512 to 1023 and are 10 bits long, direct addressing is unusable with user add-ons.

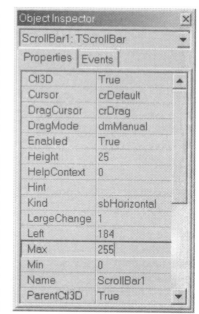

Fig.7.3 Altering the Max setting

Reading

A slightly longer routine is needed in order to read from a port, but the process is still quite straightforward. The example program shown here reads from the printer port at base address 888 (&H378), and the port must obviously be a bidirectional type. The program is assigned to a timer component having an interval of about 25 ms. Note that the program requires a label component, which must be included on the form. This component is needed to provide the program with somewhere to print the readings.

```
begin
asm
push dx
mov dx, 890
mov al, 32
```

```
out dx, al
mov dx, 888
in al, dx
mov InVal, al
pop dx
end;
Str (InVal, S);
Label1.Caption := S;
end;
```

As in the port writing program, first the contents of the dx register are pushed onto the Stack. A value of 32 is output to address 890 to set the data lines of the printer port to the input mode. Then the address of the printer port's data lines is loaded into the dx register, and the data read from the port is loaded into the al register. The variable called "InVal" is then used to store the contents of the al register. In other words, the value read from the port is moved into and stored in variable "inVal". Finally, the original contents of the dx register are restored from the Stack, and the routine is then terminated.

The value stored in "InVal" must now be printed on the screen, and this can be achieved using normal Object Pascal instructions. These start by placing the value in "InVal" into string variable "S". The latter is then assigned to the label component where it is displayed on the screen. Do not forget that Delphi requires all variables to be declared. The byte and string variables called "InVal" and "S" must therefore be declared in the appropriate section of the program or error messages will be generated.

The inline assembler is included in Delphi 1, and these methods of reading and writing will work with this version of Delphi. However, the Port function would seem to be the better option when using Delphi 1. It is so easy to use the assembler to access the ports that it is probably best to opt for this method and a later version of Delphi. Many of the improvements in the later versions are of little importance when producing software for your PC projects, but there are some general improvements that make programming life easier. Input and output functions can be defined and then called up when required, but it is probably easier to simply paste in the assembly language routines as and when they are required.

Remember that Delphi 2, 3, etc., produce 32-bit programs that are suitable for Windows 95, 98, and ME, but not Windows 3.1. Also remember that direct port accessing is not permitted with Windows NT4, 2000, and XP.

Even using the inline assembler, these operating systems will intercept and block attempts to directly write to a port or read from it.

Visual BASIC

On the face of it, Visual BASIC is ideal for producing software for use with your PC projects. It is powerful, relatively easygoing, and makes it easy to produce fancy user interfaces having buttons, large digital readouts, and analogue displays. The big drawback is that no version of this programming language, from the original MS-DOS version to the current 32-bit Windows variety, has included INP and OUT instructions. There is no equivalent to either of these instructions, which would seem to totally preclude Visual BASIC for use with PC add-ons.

Fortunately, there is a "get out clause" in the form of various add-ons that provide INP and OUT instructions or permit direct port accesses by some other means. A search of the Internet should produce details of several add-ons that deal with general input/output operations, or with a specific type of port such as the serial ports. There is actually a built-in module (MSComm) for handling the serial ports in Visual BASIC 6 Professional and the more upmarket versions, but not in the standard version. This module might be worthy of investigation if you intend to use the serial ports a great deal, but it is not well suited to all types of serial port use.

For most purposes the majority of the input/output add-ons have a large amount of overkill. The software for the average PC project requires nothing more than the straightforward INP and OUT instructions used in other versions of BASIC. In fact these are sufficient for most projects, including the more complex types. Fortunately, there is a freeware add-on that adds these instructions to Visual BASIC. It is genuinely freeware, and using it therefore costs nothing apart from any costs involved in downloading it from the Internet. The Zip file for inpout32 is only about 20 kilobytes, so it downloads almost instantly. Unlike many other Visual BASIC plug-ins, it is also very easy to install and use. Having installed it, the INP and OUT instructions operate just like any other Visual BASIC instructions.

Inpout32

This add-on is available from more than one web-site, but the obvious place to go is the excellent web site of its originator, Jan Axelson. This site is at www.lvr.com, and here you will find a lot of information about

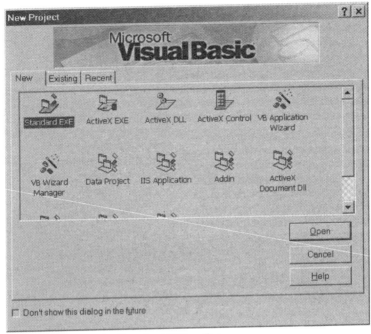

Fig.7.4 Selectect the Standard EXE option

interfacing PCs, plus links to numerous sites that have further information on this subject. If you are interested in interfacing PCs this is definitely a site you should study. There are two versions of the download, called Input16 and Input32. These are respectively for 16 and 32-bit versions of Visual BASIC. Here only the 32-bit version will be considered.

A dynamic link library (DLL) file, which seems to be an easier option than the alternatives such as an ActiveX control, provides the additional instructions. The download contains several files in addition to the DLL file, and one of these is a text file that contains instructions on using the DLL file. However, this process will be briefly covered here so that you can see how simple the process is without having to download the files first. The first step is to run Visual BASIC, and it is assumed here that you are using Visual BASIC 6. The inpout32.dll file also works with Visual BASIC 5, but note that this has a slightly different menu structure. This might necessitate minor alterations to the instructions provided here. It might also be usable with other visual programming languages, but I have not tried to use it with any others.

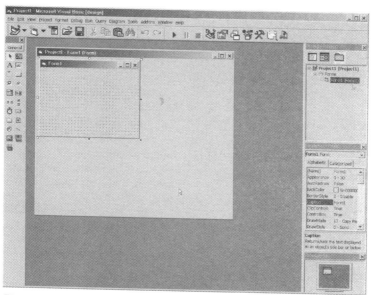

Fig.7.5 The screen layout in Visual BASIC 6.0

On launching Visual BASIC 6 you get the initial screen shown in Figure 7.4. This offers the option of producing several types of program, and it is normal EXE file that is needed for PC add-ons. Select the "Standard.EXE" icon and then operate the Open button. This takes you into the main Visual BASIC program, which has a multi-window set-up that it is broadly similar to the one used for Delphi (Figure 7.5). There is a form with a grid of dots where the program window is designed. There is a menu bar and a toolbar at the top of the main window.

Down the left-hand side of the main window there is a palette containing components that can be placed on the form. The usual items are available here, such as a timer, buttons, and a textbox. On the other side of the main window and towards the top, there is a window that shows the constituent parts of the program. There is not much here initially, and there will normally be just a single form, which will be called "form1" by default. You can use this window to select items and switch them on and off in the main window. It is probably of more use with large programs than the more simple variety that will normally be used with your PC add-ons.

The window beneath this one is the Properties window, and it shows the properties of any item that is selected. This item will usually be a form or components on the form. An item can be selected using any standard Windows method, such as left clicking on any non-active part of it. The Properties window does not simply show the current size of objects, their position, and so on. The parameters shown in this window can be edited, and this permits components to be sized and positioned more accurately than by dragging them. It also gives access to parameters that can not be adjusted via the dragging method, such as the interval of a timer component and the font used for the lettering in a textbox.

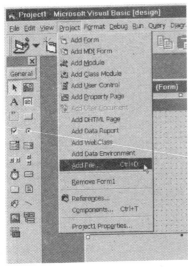

Fig.7.6 Select the Add File option

The bottom window on the right-hand side of the screen shows a representation of a monitor with the current program shown on its screen. As the form is resized, its representation in this window will change accordingly. The representation of the program window can be dragged to any desired position on the screen, and this will be used as the starting position for the real program when it is run.

Inpout32.bas

In order to add the INP and OUT instructions to Visual BASIC it is necessary to have two files in place. The first of these is Inpout32.dll, which was mentioned earlier. This must be moved to a folder on the hard disc that will enable Windows to find it, and probably the best place is in the C:\Windows\System folder. This is not sufficient in itself to add the INP and OUT instructions. Visual BASIC must be told how and when to use this DLL file. This is achieved using the second file, which is called Inpout32.bas, which is included in the Inpout32 download. This file must be loaded into your programs, or projects as they are called in Visual BASIC terminology, in order to bring Inpout32.dll into operation.

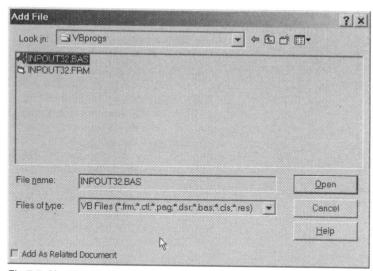

Fig.7.7 Use the file browser to locate and open Inpout32.bas

Loading Inpout32.bas into a Visual BASIC project is very easy, and it is just a matter of going to the Project menu and selecting the Add File option (Figure 7.6). This produces the usual file browser (Figure 7.7) where you can locate and open the file. This should result in a Module entry appearing in the list of items used in the program, and expanding this entry should confirm that Inpout32.BAS has been added (Figure 7.8). The INP and OUT instructions will then work properly, and in use will be no different to any of the standard Visual BASIC commands.

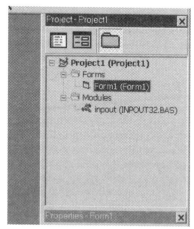

Fig.7.8 The project now includes Inpout32

First steps

It is advisable to try some simple programming exercises before getting deep into "real" programs for PC add-ons. These will help to familiarise you with Visual

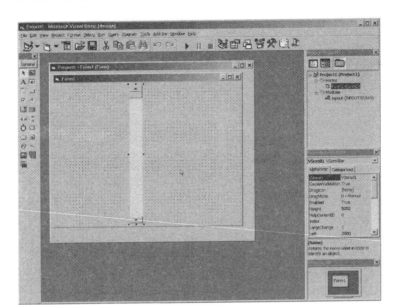

Fig.7.9 A vertical scrollbar has been added to the form

BASIC's method of working, and will check that the newly added instructions are working properly. To confirm that the OUT instruction is functioning correctly, start by placing a scrollbar on the form. It is probably best to drag the form to a slightly larger size first so that it can accommodate a fairly large scrollbar. Both horizontal and vertical versions are available from the palette of components, and their icons are easily recognised. However, if you are not sure which component a particular icon represents, placing the pointer over the icon will result in a brief description appearing.

In order to place the scrollbar on the form it is just a matter of left clicking the icon for the appropriate type of scrollbar, and then dragging a rectangle onto the form. In other words, position the pointer on the form, hold down the left mouse button, and then move the pointer to a new position on the form before releasing the left button. You do not have to bother about getting the size and position of a component right first time. Once on the form, the usual handles appear whenever a component is selected. A newly added component is automatically selected, so you can use the handles to drag it to a new size. To move a component, simply position the pointer anywhere on the component and then drag it to a new position.

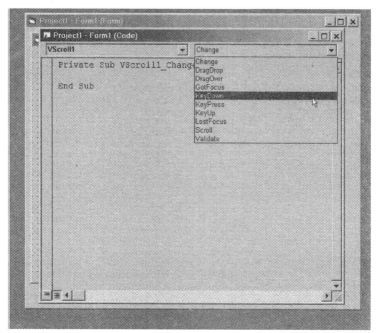

Fig.7.10 This menu offers a full range of events

You should now have something like Figure 7.9, and in this example a vertical scrollbar has been added. Now double-click on the scrollbar, and this will bring the Code window to the front. Two lines of code will be added automatically for the scrollbar, which will be called "Vscroll1" by default, or "Hscroll1" if you are using a horizontal scrollbar. The first line starts with the word "Private", and the second line is "End Sub". These mark the beginning and the end of the subroutine for the scrollbar. You have to add the code that will make the scrollbar do something, and this code is added between these two lines.

It is important to realise that Visual BASIC programs are event driven, and the code you write is therefore assigned to a component and to an event. The available events vary from one component to another, as does the event used by default. The first line in the subroutine indicates the event that will activate your code, and in this example the word "Change" appears in this line. In other words, an event is generated when the setting of the scrollbar is altered. The other options are available from one of the menus at the top of the Code window (Figure 7.10). The default option will usually be the one that you need, as it is in this example.

Adding code

The purpose of this demonstration program is to permit the value output
to printer port 1 to be altered using the scrollbar. All the code has to do
is take the value from Vscroll1 and output it to the correct address. There
is no need to bother about loops or other program structures. An event
is generated each time the scrollbar's setting is changed, and the code
used in the subroutine will therefore be executed each time a new value
is produced. This single line of code is all that is needed if a vertical
scrollbar is used:

```
OUT &H378,VScroll1.Value
```

Use this version for a horizontal scrollbar:

```
OUT &H378,HScroll1.Value
```

The OUT instruction is used to send data to the printer port, and the
address used here will normally be correct for printer port 1. This address
should obviously be changed accordingly if you are using a printer port
at a different base address. The value read from the scrollbar is placed
in a variable called VScroll1.Value (or HScroll1.Value), and it is the
contents of this variable that are output to the printer port. The variables
associated with Visual BASIC components all take this basic form, with
the name of the component being used as the first part of the variable's
name. Next there is a full stop, and then the name of the parameter.

If you are not sure of the correct name to use, select the component and
then look through the settings available in the Properties window. The
parameter you wish to use will be listed here under the correct name to
use in variables. Note that practically any parameter listed in the
Properties window can be used in programs via the appropriate variable.
In this example the variable is being used to read from a component, but
in most cases it is possible to alter parameters by changing the relevant
variable. This method can be used to change the size and position of
components, alter their colour, change the text on labels, and so on.

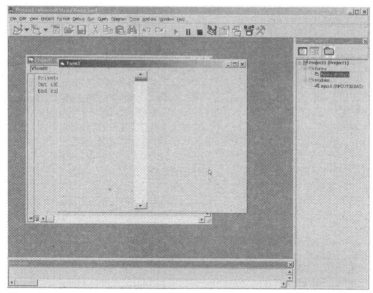

Fig.7.11 The grid of dots does not appear when the compiled program is run

Scaling

With the line of code added, the program is not yet ready for testing. By default, the minimum value produced by the scrollbar is zero, but the maximum value is some 32767. Some mathematics could be used to obtain the required maximum value of 255, but there is an easier way of handling things. With the scrollbar selected, find the Max (maximum value) parameter in the Properties window and alter it to 255.

There are two other parameters associated with changes in the scrollbar's value. Small Change is the amount by which the value changes when one of the arrows at each end of the bar is left-clicked. The default value of one is suitable in this case. Large Change is the amount of change produced by left clicking immediately above or below the control knob of the scrollbar. This will probably be reduced to one when the maximum value is reduced to 255. You may prefer to use a larger value here such as 5 or 10.

The program is then ready for testing. You do not have to compile the program to an EXE file in order to test it. Programs can be run inside Visual BASIC by going to the Run menu and selecting either Start or

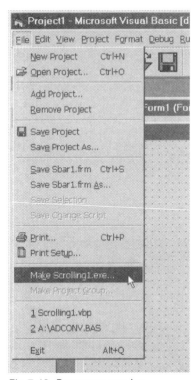

Start With Full Compile. The second option is the more thorough and reliable way of testing programs, but either option will suffice for checking this simple program. Assuming the code has been entered correctly, the new program window should appear, complete with the scrollbar but minus the grid of dots on the form (Figure 7.11). Try the scrollbar at various settings while monitoring the outputs of the printer port. Note that with a vertical scrollbar, zero is produced with the scrollbar's control knob at the top, and not as one might have thought, at the bottom. The zero setting for a horizontal scrollbar is, as one would expect, obtained with the control knob at the extreme left-hand position.

Fig.7.12 Programs can be compiled to EXE files

Compiling

With interpreted programming languages such as GW BASIC and QBASIC there is no option other than running your programs from within the programming language. Visual BASIC, like Delphi, is a compiled language and it can produce standalone programs. Actually, this is not strictly true, and there are a few ifs, buts, and maybes with Visual BASIC. Visual BASIC programs are often remarkably small, but they are not true standalone programs. It is not a fully compiled language, and it is reliant on the PC having so-called runtime modules installed.

This is not usually a problem, as these modules are installed as part of a normal Windows installation. Difficulties will only occur if you try to run Visual BASIC programs on a PC that has a customised Windows installation that lacks the runtime modules. Installing the missing modules should clear the problem. Note that when Visual BASIC compiles a standalone program, the program file it produces will need any special DLL files in addition to the normal runtime modules. In the current context

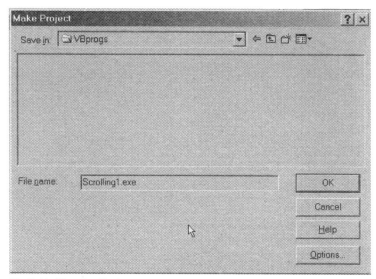

Fig.7.13 Use the file browser to select the destination for the compiled program file

this means that Inpout32.dll must accompany the program file. The program should work perfectly well with Inpout32.dll in the C:\Windows\System directory, or in the same folder as the program file. The easiest way of handling things is to always have this file in the same folder as the program file.

With simple programs Visual BASIC produces a pseudo standalone program file, but with more complex projects it might produce a program group instead. In other words, it will produce a group of files that includes a Setup program. The Setup program is used to install the main program in standard Windows fashion. The simple port writing program will compile to a standalone EXE file, and this is the option that will be offered by the File menu (Figure 7.12). Selecting this option produces the usual file browser (Figure 7.13) where you can select the destination folder and, if desired, change the name of the program. Operate the OK button to generate the EXE program file.

To test the new program file, minimise Visual BASIC and launch Windows Explorer. Use Windows Explorer to locate the program file and then double-click on its entry to run the program. This should produce the same program window and scrollbar as before, and the program should control the printer port in the same manner as before. However, this

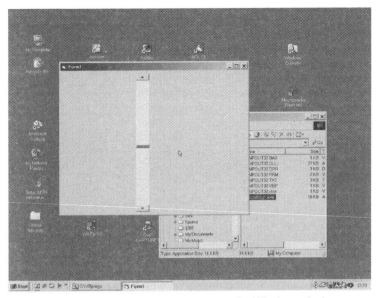

Fig.7.14 The compiled program running on the Windows desktop

time the program will operate on the Windows desktop independently of
Visual BASIC (Figure 7.14). The program should continue to operate if
Visual BASIC is closed down, but save the scrollbar project first so that
you can continue experimenting with it later. Try putting the program file
and Inpout32.dll onto a floppy disc, and then try running the program on
another PC. The program should run properly even if that PC does not
have Visual BASIC installed.

Refining

It is easy to add a few refinements to the program, and the most obvious
one is to have a digital readout that shows the value being output to the
printer port. Return to Visual BASIC and, if it is not already loaded, open
the scrollbar project. Select the label component (its icon is the one that
contains the letter "A") and then place a large label component on the
form using the normal dragging process. It might be necessary to
reposition the scrollbar or increase the size of the form in order to make
a suitable space for the label component.

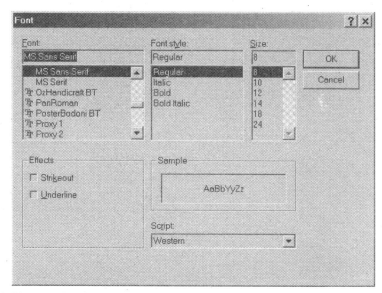

Fig.7.15 The font window provides the usual size options, etc.

The label will be called Label1 by default. It is possible to change the name of any component using the Properties window, and forms can be renamed using the same method. With very simple programs there is probably no point in doing so, but it can be beneficial to use a more meaningful name with more complex programs. It is definitely a good idea if there are several components of the same type. Renaming the components then makes it easier to remember the function of each one. Try renaming this label component as "Readout". The name of a component is always the first parameter listed in the Properties window incidentally.

The default text on the label is its initial name, or Label1 in this case. This text is not required when the program is run, and it is only added by Visual BASIC so that you can see the default font, text size, etc., used for the label. Use the Caption parameter in the Properties window to change the text to read "255", so that the text is more representative of what will appear on the label when the program is run. You can then experiment with the text size, font, colour, etc., to get the label's appearance exactly as you require.

For the present application the default text size is rather small, and it is a good idea to set a much larger size. Doubling clicking on the Font entry

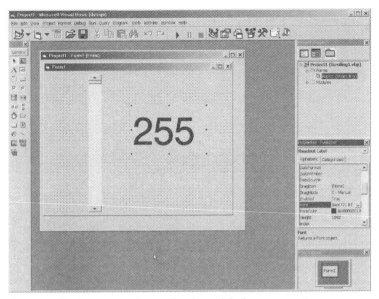

Fig.7.16 The form, complete with a large label component

in the Properties window launches the window shown in Figure 7.15. Here the installed fonts are available in their usual range of sizes, as are the standard font styles and effects. In Figure 7.16 the Swiss 721 font is used, and the text size has been set at a massive 72 points. There are other useful parameters available via the Properties window, and you can alter the text colour, background colour, the text justification type, and border style.

Auto-sizing

You can also enable the automatic sizing option. When this is enabled, the size of the label is automatically adjusted so that it is always just big enough to accommodate its caption text. This avoids the possibility of text being clipped due to the label being too small, but always make sure that the form is able to accommodate the label at its largest size.

No text is required initially, other than the text written to the label by the program. Therefore, delete the caption when you have set all the parameters to your satisfaction. Then double-click the scrollbar to bring up the Code window, and add this line of code after the line entered previously:

```
Readout.Caption = VScroll1.Value
```

Obviously HScroll1 should be substituted for VScroll1 if you are using a horizontal scrollbar. All this line does is to write the value read from the scrollbar to the label each time that the position of the scrollbar is altered.

If you try running the program it will look something like Figure 7.17 initially, with no value displayed on the label. This happens because the program is event driven, and no event is generated until the position of the scrollbar is altered. A value is then output to the printer port, and the same value is displayed on the label (Figure 7.18).

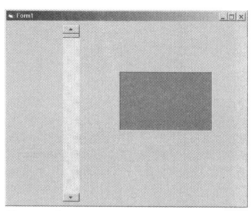

Fig.7.17 The label is blank when the program is launched

If it is important for an initial level to be output at startup, this is easily accomplished. Double-click on the form to bring up the Code window. The cursor will be on a blank line in the skeleton subroutine for the form. This subroutine will be performed when the form is loaded, or when the program is launched in other words. Try adding the appropriate line of code for the type of scrollbar you are using:

```
VScroll1.Value = 240
HScroll1.Value = 240
```

This sets the value of the scrollbar to 240 when the program is launched. The initial value of the scrollbar is zero by default, so this constitutes a change in the value of the scrollbar. Accordingly, the subroutine assigned to the scrollbar is activated, causing a value of 240 to be written to the

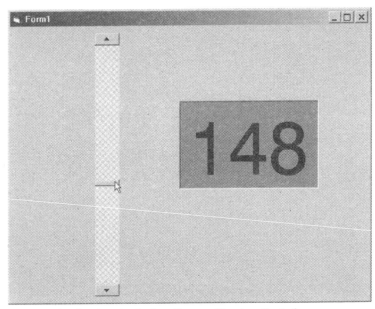

Fig.7.18 A value is output when the scrollbar is adjusted

printer port and to the caption of the label component (Figure 7.19). Of course, the scrollbar's control knob also responds to the change and takes up its new position.

Any initial value can be produced using this method, apart from zero. The problem with setting the scrollbar's value to zero is simply that it starts at this value anyway. Consequently, no change in value is produced, and the subroutine assigned to the scrollbar is not

Fig.7.19 The program can start by outputting a value other than zero

activated at startup. One way around this problem is to use two lines of code in the subroutine for the form. The first would output a value of zero to the printer port, and the second would write zero to the label's caption.

An easier way of doing things is to use a single program line in the subroutine for the form. This sets

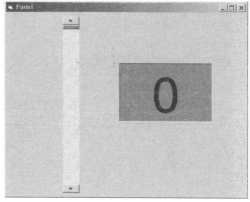

Fig.7.20 Starting with a value of zero

the value to zero using essentially the same line of code provided previously. The initial value of the scrollbar is then set to anything other than zero using the Properties window. The scrollbar starts at a non-zero value when the program is launched, and its value is then changed to zero by the form's subroutine. This activates the subroutine for the scrollbar, resulting in zero being written to both the printer port and the label (Figure 7.20).

Although the event driven system of Visual BASIC enables complex tasks to be achieved using simple program code, this demonstrates the point that you have to keep your wits about you. It is essential to think carefully about the way programs will respond to events if programming errors are to be avoided. You also have to make sure you understand exactly what triggers an event before you try to use it in your programs. Otherwise the finished program might be remarkably inactive due to events not being triggered as expected. Worse still, programs can run out of control due to unexpected events being generated.

Inverting

The positions of items on the form and their sizes are set using screen co-ordinates. The scaling seems to be arbitrary, and screen co-ordinates do not operate on a one pixel per co-ordinate basis. The ratio is nearer one pixel for every 10 screen co-ordinates. Co-ordinate 0,0 is in the top right-hand corner of the form, and not the bottom left-hand corner as one might have expected. This results in some things working in what

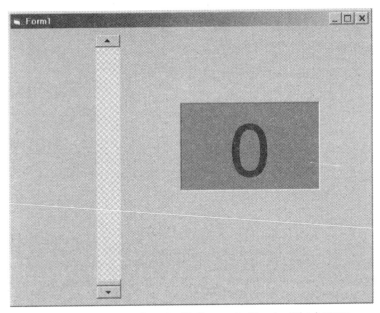

Fig.7.21 Zero is now produced with the control knob at the bottom

might be regarded as an upside-down fashion, including vertical scrollbars. As already pointed out, the minimum value is produced with the control knob at the top, and the value reduces as the slider is moved downwards.

It is easy to correct this, and it is just a matter of subtracting the value read from the scrollbar from the maximum value it can produce. In this case the maximum value is 255, so deducting the value read from the scrollbar from 255 gives the required inversion. A value of 0 is produced with the control knob at the bottom, running through to 255 with it at the top of its travel. The port writing program is easily modified to operate in this fashion. Start by double clicking on the form to bring up its code in the Code window. Then erase any existing code assigned to the form and replace it with this line:

```
Vscroll1.Value = 255
```

Fig.7.22 Moving the knob upwards produces an increase in the value output to the port

Next, move down to the subroutine for the scrollbar, erase the existing code, and insert these three lines instead:

```
Inverted = 255 - VScroll1.Value
Out &H378, Inverted
Readout.Caption = Inverted
```

In both cases, only erase the program code that you added previously. The two lines per subroutine added by Visual BASIC should be left intact, with the new code being added between these lines. You should get something like Figure 7.21 when the program is run, with the control knob at the bottom and "0" displayed on the digital readout. Moving the knob towards the top of its track should result in the value output being increased, as shown by the digital readout in Figure 7.22.

The line of code assigned to the form simply sets the scrollbar at an initial value of 255, which sets the knob at its lowest position. The first line in the scrollbar's subroutine inverts values read from the scrollbar.

The inverted values are then written to the printer port and the digital readout by the next two lines.

Port selection

As things stand, the address range for the printer port has to be altered by changing the program code. This is acceptable if you are only writing programs for your own use, but it is still a bit inflexible. You can return to the source code and recompile the program, but this is a slow and clumsy way of handling things. It is not a good way of doing things if your programs will be distributed to others. They either manage to use the right port address or they do not use your program. Changing the code and recompiling the program is not an option for them.

It is easy enough to add buttons so that the required address range can be selected once the program has been launched. Start by adding a couple of buttons to the form. If necessary, enlarge the form and (or) move the existing components around in order to make room for the buttons. Change the caption for the first button (Command1) to "632", and change the caption for the second button (Command2) to "888". These are what will usually be the base addresses for printer ports 2 and 1 respectively. The default text size is quite small, so it is advisable to use the Font setting in the Properties window to set a larger size of about 18 points.

Shortcuts

If you try using something like "&H378" as the text string for a button you will find that the "&" character does not appear on the button. Instead, the "H" character will be underlined. The ampersand (&) character is used as a means of designating keyboard shortcuts. In this example it appears ahead of the "H" character, and operating Alt and H keys provides a keyboard alternative to left-clicking the button using the mouse. The "H" character is underlined to indicate to users that this shortcut is available. Keyboard shortcuts are not normally of any real use with simple programs, but you can add them if you wish. The "&H" prefix should not be used on buttons, etc. Instead, either use decimal addresses or something like "Hex 278" for a hexadecimal address.

Returning to the port selection program, normally a program is fully active as soon as it is launched, but in this case it is preferable for it to be suppressed until a port address has been selected. This avoids the possibility of the program operating with the wrong address. The easy way of having the program inactive initially is to use the Properties window to disable the scrollbar and the label. Select each one in turn, and set the Enabled property to False. The buttons must activate subroutines that select the appropriate port address and then switch on the scrollbar and the label. Bring the Code window to the front and edit the listing to make it the same as the one provided here:

```
Dim Port1 As Integer

Private Sub Command1_Click()
Port1 = 632
Readout.Enabled = True
VScroll1.Enabled = True
End Sub

Private Sub Command2_Click()
Port1 = 888
Readout.Enabled = True
VScroll1.Enabled = True
End Sub

Private Sub Form_Load()
VScroll1.Value = 255
End Sub

Private Sub VScroll1_Change()
Inverted = 255 - VScroll1.Value
Out Port1, Inverted
Readout.Caption = Inverted
End Sub
```

The first line is outside any of the subroutines, and this is important. It is declaring the variable called Port1 as an integer variable, and this is the variable that is used to hold the selected port address. If this variable originated in a subroutine it would be a private type. In other words, it would be inaccessible to parts of the program outside that subroutine. This property can be useful, but here we require a global variable that

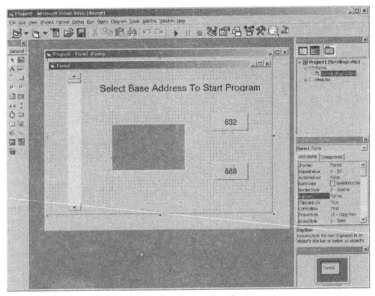

Fig.7.23 The completed form for the revised program

can be altered in one subroutine and then accessed by another subroutine. This can be achieved by declaring the variable outside a subroutine.

Essentially the same subroutine is used for each button. First variable Port1 is set at the apposite base address for the button concerned. Then the label and the scrollbar are enabled, which effectively starts the program. When the setting of the scrollbar is altered, the Out instruction in its subroutine uses Port1 to provide the address, so the address used here depends on the button that the user operates.

If you try this program you can add a label to the form indicating that operating a button selects the appropriate port address and starts the program. It is always a good idea to make it as clear as possible to users how a program is used, rather than simply leaving them to operate buttons and menus and see what happens. With the form completed, you should have soothing like Figure 7.23. When initially run, the program should look similar to Figure 7.24, with the scrollbar and readout label inoperative. Operating one of the buttons will bring both into action, as in Figure 7.25. Provided the right port address is selected, operating the scrollbar should alter the value output to the relevant printer port.

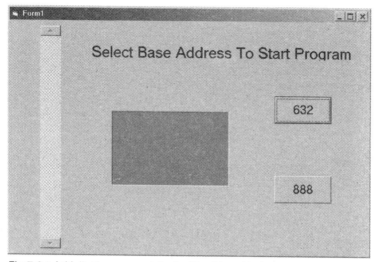

Fig.7.24 Initially the program looks like this, with the scrollbar and the label both inoperative

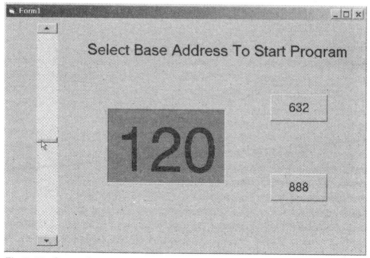

Fig.7.25 Operating one of the buttons activates the label and the scrollbar

Now you see it

Apart from components that never appear when the program is run, there is a Visible parameter that can be used to make components appear or disappear. This can often be useful, and with this simple program it can be used to hide the readout label and the scrollbar initially. They can be made to appear when a button is operated, and the buttons can then be hidden. This sort of thing is quite normal in Windows programming, and it avoids having a confusing user interface that is cluttered with things that do not actually do anything. This is the modified version of the program:

```
Dim Port1 As Integer

Private Sub Command1_Click()
Port1 = 632
Readout.Enabled = True
Readout.Visible = True
VScroll1.Enabled = True
VScroll1.Visible = True
Command1.Visible = False
Command2.Visible = False
Label1.Caption = "Use Scrollbar To Adjust Port
Value"
End Sub

Private Sub Command2_Click()
Port1 = 888
Readout.Enabled = True
Readout.Visible = True
VScroll1.Enabled = True
VScroll1.Visible = True
Command1.Visible = False
Command2.Visible = False
Label1.Caption = "Use Scrollbar To Adjust Port
Value"
End Sub
```

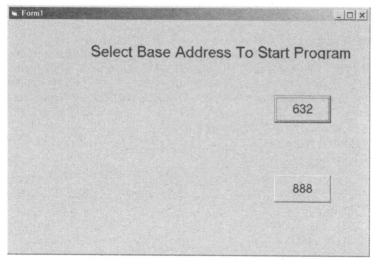

Fig.7.26 Initially, neither the scrollbar nor the label is displayed

```
Private Sub Form_Load()
VScroll1.Value = 255
End Sub

Private Sub VScroll1_Change()
Inverted = 255 - VScroll1.Value
Out Port1, Inverted
Readout.Caption = Inverted
End Sub
```

For this program to have the desired effect the Visible parameter for the readout label and the scrollbar should be set False using the Properties window. This prevents them from appearing when the program is launched. The additions to the program are in the subroutines for the two command buttons, and they are the same for both buttons. Two lines are used to set the Visible parameter for the readout label and the scrollbar at True. This causes both components to appear when a button is operated. Two further additions set the Visible parameter for each button at False, causing both buttons to disappear when either button is operated. A fifth additional line provides a further refinement, which is to have the onscreen instruction change to something more appropriate

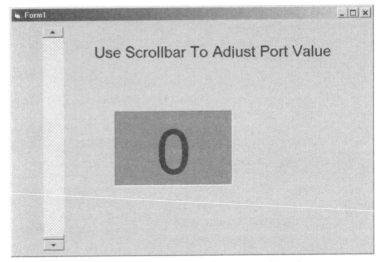

Fig.7.27 Operating a button produces the appropriate changes

for the program once it is underway. An alternative would be to simply render the label invisible.

When initially run the program should look something like Figure 7.26, with neither the readout label or the scrollbar in evidence. Operating one of the buttons with result in a change to something more like Figure 7.27, with the digital readout and the scrollbar appearing, and the two buttons disappearing. The instruction label should also change.

Reading

So far only writing to a port has been considered, but reading from a port is very straightforward using Visual BASIC. It is just a matter of using the INP instruction to read the port, and then using the value read from the port as the caption for a label. This is much the same as the method used previously with Delphi, but Visual BASIC is much more easy-going. There is no need to convert the numeric variable to a string type before using it as the caption. The numeric variable can be used as the caption, and Visual BASIC will automatically convert it to the appropriate string of characters. This is essentially the same way that traditional BASIC programming languages work. With GW BASIC and QBASIC for example, it is not necessary to convert a variable to a string before printing it on the screen.

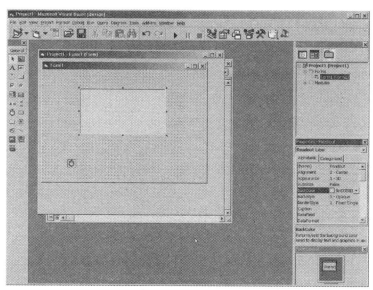

Fig.7.28 The label and the timer added to the form

To try out reading a port, start with a new project and install Inpout32.bas. Then enlarge the form slightly from its default size. Add a label component and make it large enough to take a three-digit readout having large digits. Rename this component as "Readout" and delete its default caption. Set a large font size and make any other changes you require, such as altering the justification or the colour scheme.

Next, add a timer component to the form. The icon for this component is the one that looks like a stopwatch. This component is not displayed when the program is run, so its position on the form is unimportant. Components of this type can be positioned anywhere

Fig.7.29 The finished program in action

that keeps them clear of other components. In order to use the Visual BASIC timer component it is essential to set its time interval using the Properties window. The default time is zero milliseconds, which effectively switches off the timer. In this application the timer's interval parameter sets the gap between successive readings, or the frequency of readings if you prefer to view things that way. An interval of 100 milliseconds gives 10 readings per second, and this will usually give good results.

To complete the program it is merely necessary to assign a few lines of code to the timer component. Double-click on the timer to bring up the Code window, and then add these two lines of code into the timer's subroutine:

```
Out &H37A,32
Readout.Caption = Inp(&H378)
```

You should now have screen something like Figure 7.28, and when the program is tested it should look similar to Figure 7.29. Inputting various values to printer port 1 should result in the appropriate values being displayed on the digital readout. The first program line assigned to the timer component simply sets what will normally be printer port 1 to act as an input port. The second line reads the data lines of the port and prints the result via the caption of the label component.

Refinements

An obvious refinement to the program is to add some means of setting the correct addresses for the printer port. This time three radio buttons will be used to select one of the three standard address ranges. Start by making the form wider so that there is space for the buttons and their captions to the right of the digital display. Then place three of these buttons on the form, one above the other, in this space. Note that in Visual BASIC terminology the radio buttons are called option buttons. Change the captions of the three buttons, as detailed here:

Button	Caption
Option1	Hex 3BC
Option2	Hex 378
Option3	Hex 278

Next, add an ordinary command button below the display and change its caption to "START". Then select the timer component and set its Enabled parameter at False using the Properties window. Finally, go to the Code window and replace the existing program with this one:

```
Dim Prn1 As Integer
Dim Prn2 As Integer

Private Sub Command1_Click()
Timer1.Enabled = True
Option1.Visible = False
Option2.Visible = False
Option3.Visible = False
End Sub

Private Sub Option1_Click()
Prn1 = &H3BC
Prn2 = &H3BE
End Sub

Private Sub Option2_Click()
Prn1 = &H378
Prn2 = &H37A
End Sub

Private Sub Option3_Click()
Prn1 = &H278
Prn2 = &H27A
End Sub

Private Sub Timer1_Timer()
Out Prn2, 32
Readout.Caption = Inp(Prn1)
End Sub
```

The first two lines declare two global variables (Prn1 and Prn2), and these will be used to store the two port addresses used in the timer component's subroutine. The subroutine for each option button merely

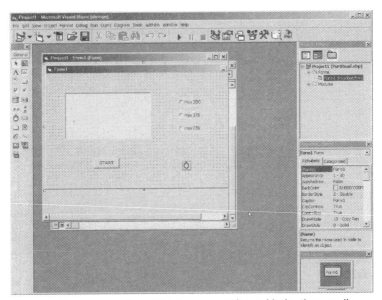

Fig.7.30 The new version of the form, complete with the three radio buttons that are used to select the port address range

assigns the appropriate two addresses to these variables. At this stage the timer component is switched off and no readings are being taken, so it does not matter if the option buttons default to the wrong address. Once the right address has been selected, operating the START button (Command1) gets the program underway. The subroutine for Command1 enables the timer component, and then it renders the three option buttons invisible. This ensures that the port addresses can not be accidentally altered once the program has started taking readings.

If you try this program you should end up with something like Figure 7.30, and the program should look like Figure 7.31 when it is launched. Use the radio buttons to select the correct port base address. When you select a button, the previously selected button is deselected. It is therefore impossible to select more than one option using a bank of these buttons. They are usually termed radio buttons, because they are similar in use to the waveband buttons that used to feature on many radio sets.

If the default button (Option1) is the correct button, there is no need to left-click it. Its code will have been performed when the program started, and the two variables will already have the correct values. The program

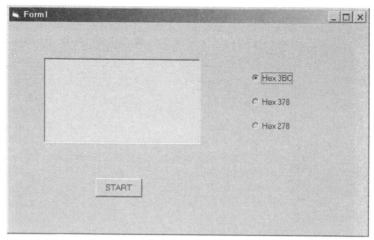

Fig.7.31 The port reading program as it appears initially

should change to something like Figure 7.32 when the START button is operated. The display will start to produce readings and the three radio buttons will disappear, effectively rendering them inactive.

Analogue display

Using Visual BASIC it is easy to do things like pseudo analogue displays, and for this example readings from the printer port will be displayed via the computer equivalent of a panel meter. It would no doubt be possible to produce a meter having a curved scale like the real thing, but with the computerised version it is easier to have a scale that is straight and a pointer that varies in length so that it always reaches the scale. In practice this arrangement is no easier or more difficult to read than a conventional scale, so it is a perfectly valid approach.

Start with a new project and enlarge the form slightly so that there is room for a decent sized meter. Select the shape component from the palette and then drag a square onto the form in a central position near the bottom. By default the shape will be transparent, so set BackStyle (background style) to Opaque and the FillStyle to Solid using the Properties window. Then select the desired border and fill colours (BorderColor and FillColor respectively). The shape is a rectangle by default, but you may prefer to use a different shape. Others, such as

Fig.7.32 The port reading program in full operation

oval and circle, are available via the Properties window. I used a circle for this shape, which represents the coil, etc., of the meter, and provides the pivot point for the pointer.

Next, select the line component from the palette and drag a vertical line from the middle of the shape to somewhere near the top of the form. This line represents the pointer of the meter, and the default settings are perfectly all right. However, you can change its width, colour, etc., should you wish to do so. Do not take the line too close to the top of the form because this would not leave enough space for the calibration marks and labels. At this point you should have something resembling Figure 7.33.

Meter scale

We now require a series of short vertical lines across the form to provide the scale for the meter. You can add a large number of these if you wish, but bear in mind that the meter will have to be quite large in order to accommodate a substantial number of calibration ticks. If you try to overdo this aspect of the display you might find that when the program is run the scale looks uneven. It is even possible that some of the calibration ticks would fail to appear when the program was run on some PCs. The Visual BASIC co-ordinate system can tend to lull you into a

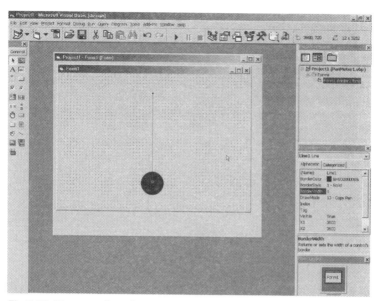

Fig.7.33 The meter's pointer and pivot point added to the form

false sense of security, and you have to bear in mind that there will normally be far fewer pixels than screen co-ordinates.

For the sake of this example we will settle for a simple scale having about two dozen calibration ticks. However, the same basic process can be used to provide a finer scale if desired. Readings from the printer port run from 0 to 255, but here we will settle for a more convenient scale of 0 to 250. This does not fully utilise the eight-bit resolution of the port, but the loss of resolution is too small to be of any real significance.

With the pointer at its mid setting, the Properties window showed this line to have an X co-ordinate of 3600. Obviously the X co-ordinate is likely to be different on your version, but you can correct this by dragging the pointer and the circle into the appropriate position. To select two objects, either drag a rectangle around them using the arrow tool in the component palette, or left-click on one, hold down the Control key, and then left-click on the second object. Both methods can be used to select numerous objects incidentally.

It is possible for the pointer to go 2500 units either side of its central position without getting too close to either edge of the form, and this

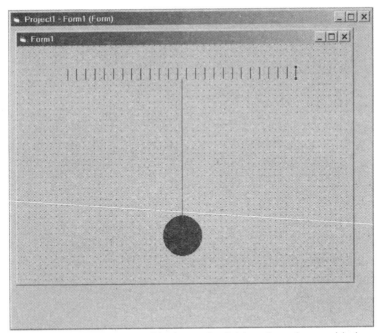

Fig.7.34 The lines that provide the scale divisions have been added to the form

gives convenient scaling. With the pointer covering a total of 5000 units and the port readings going from 0 to 250, this works out at 20 screen units per input unit (5000/250 = 20). The first calibration tick is at an X co-ordinate of 1100 (3600 – 2500 = 1100). The top of the pointer is used as the baseline for the scale, so it is a matter of drawing a line (say) two grid points high with its base on the same row of dots as the top of the pointer.

Sometimes the grid will obligingly snap objects to suitable co-ordinates, but in most cases it will be necessary to do some "fine tuning" using the Properties window. In this case the X1 and X2 values for the line must both be set at 1100. The horizontal starting point of the line is therefore unimportant, since final position in this plane will be set via the Properties window. It is then a matter of adding further lines and setting them at X co-ordinates of 1300, 1500, 1700, and so on, up to a maximum 6100 (3600 + 2500). You should then have something like the form layout shown in Figure 7.34.

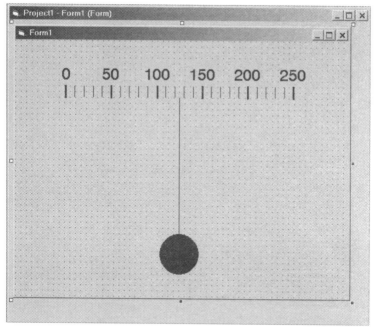

Fig.7.35 The numbers have been added to the scale and the lines for the major divisions have been widened

Figure work

Next the figures for the scale are added. I left too little room at the top of the form to accommodate the legends comfortably, so I enlarged the form, selected all the components using the arrow tool, and then dragged them a few grid points down the form. The figures are easily added using a separate label for each one. Start with the "0" legend, adjusting the font, etc., to give what you deem to be the best effect. Use the Properties window to adjust the label's position "by eye". With this type of thing it is helpful to enable the AutoSize facility. Automatic sizing ensures that none of the text will be accidentally clipped.

This process is repeated with labels at the 50, 100, 150, 200, and 250 scale ticks. The easy way to do this is to use the Copy and Paste facilities to copy the original label. Then use the Properties window to alter the text and reposition the copies. The lines at the main calibration points can be thickened slightly so that they stand out from the other calibration

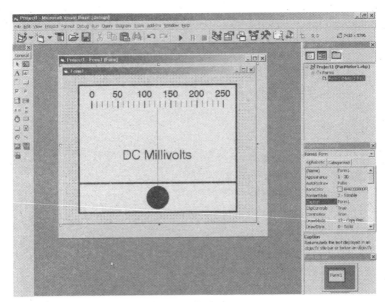

Fig.7.36 The finished panel meter design

ticks. The line width is controlled by the BorderWidth parameter, and I increased this setting from 1 to 3.

Finishing touches

When this process has been completed you should have something like the form shown in Figure 7.35. You can opt for the basic approach and simply leave it like this, or add one or two extra components to make it look a bit more like the real thing. It is certainly a good idea to at least add a label stating the units being measured (degrees Celsius, volts, amps, etc.). Making the meter look pretty will not make it work any better, but users generally prefer programs that are visually appealing, and it is worth putting a little effort into this aspect of things.

With the drawing tools available when using Visual BASIC it does not take long to add a few refinements. Figure 7.36 shows the final version of my virtual panel meter, and Figure 7.37 shows a close-up view of the form. A label has been added to show the unit of measurement, and the text has been set to a suitably large font size. When you start adding

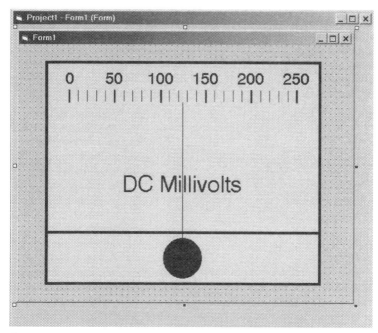

Fig.7.37 A close-up view of the form showing the finished design

refinements to an analogue display you often find that one component covers another and spoils the effect. In this example the units label was added after the line representing the pointer, and this label will therefore appear to be in front of the pointer. With a real meter this label is usually on the scale plate, and would therefore be behind the pointer.

There is an even direr example of this in the form of the shape component that is

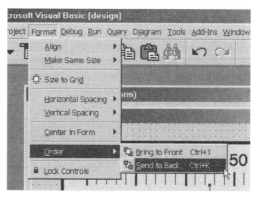

Fig.7.38 Using the Order options

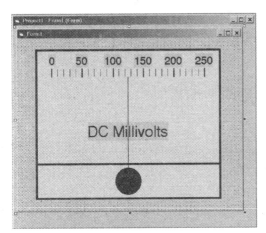

Fig.7.39 The labels do not merge with the main background

used to represent the outline of the meter. When this is initially added it is in front of everything else, and totally obscures the pointer, scale, etc. Fortunately, there is an easy way around this. Simply select an item you wish to move to the rear, go to the Format menu and select the Order option, and then select the Send to Back option (Figure 7.38). There are actually two options available from this submenu, and the other one is Send to Front. Only the appropriate one of these will be available if a component is already at the front or at the back. Both options are available for components that are sandwiched between other components. With a little experimentation you should soon manage to sort objects into a satisfactory order.

The rectangle shape used to represent the outline of the meter has to be sent to the very back, since anything behind it will be completely obscured. With the background set to a suitable colour there is a slight problem in that the background colour of the labels is unlikely to match that of the rectangle. This gives a rectangle of a different colour around each label. You might be happy with this effect (Figure 7.39), but it is easily removed by first selecting all the labels. Then use the Properties window to set the same background colour that was used for the main rectangle. The Properties window provides an easy and quick means of making this sort of en masse adjustment.

Making it work

As described so far the meter has just one major shortcoming. It looks very plausible but it does not actually do anything. The obvious way of making it read the printer port is to assign a suitable subroutine to a timer component, and this is the method that will be adopted here. Start by adding a timer component to any vacant area of the form, and then use the Properties window to set a suitable interval. It is probably best to set a fairly short interval of about 25 milliseconds so that the pointer responds rapidly and smoothly to variations in the values read from the port. With a longer interval it might jump around in an unrealistic fashion.

If you have not already installed Inpout32.bas, do so now. Then double-click on the timer component to bring up the Code window, and then add these lines of program code into the timer's subroutine:

```
Out &H37A, 32
Raw = Inp(&H378)
Raw = Raw * 20
Raw = Raw + 1100
Line1.X2 = Raw
```

The first line sets printer port 1 as an input type. Then the second line reads the data lines and stores the value in a variable called Raw. Obviously the addresses used in these lines must be changed if the printer port you are using is not at the base address of &H379. In order to move the pointer to the appropriate point on the scale it is merely necessary to alter the X2 parameter of Line1. This moves the top of the line horizontally but otherwise leaves it as before. There is no need to bother about deleting the old version of Line1 each time its position is altered, because Visual BASIC will do this automatically.

It is clearly necessary to apply some mathematics to the values read from the port in order to produce a suitable X2 value. The scale runs from an X2 value of 1100 at the left end of the scale to a value of 6100 at the right end, giving a span of 5000 screen units. The values from the port run from 0 to 250. This means that there are 20 screen units per port unit (5000/250 = 20). The value read from the port is therefore multiplied by 20 in order to get the basic scaling correct. Some further manipulation of the value is needed in order to obtain the final X2 value, because the zero point on the scale is at an X2 value of 1100. Adding 1100 to the value in Raw corrects this and produces the final value that is used as the X2 value of Line1.

Figure 7.40 shows the finished meter program in action. A value of 64 has been fed to the printer port, and the meter is providing the appropriate reading. In general, analogue and pseudo analogue displays do not provide the same degree of precision as digital types. The main

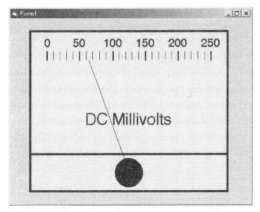

Fig.7.40 The finished program in operation

advantage of a display of this type is that you can take a rough reading at a glance. In many applications you simply require a "ball park" figure, and a high degree of precision is unnecessary.

This type of display is also preferable where readings are changing fairly rapidly. With a pointer or other analogue style display it is easy to follow readings as they rise and fall. It is very difficult to follow the blur of numbers in a digital display that is continually changing. Using a relatively slow sample rate makes reading the display much easier, but the readings might not accurately track the changes in value. An analogue display is much better for this type of thing. Of course, you do not have to settle for one type of display or the other, and in some applications it is best to include both types. With a PC based instrument you can have as many displays as you like at no extra cost.

Development

The basic meter program is easily developed into something more usable in real world applications, complete with buttons to select the required port address range and an overload warning. Figure 7.41 shows the modified form, with the additional labels and three command buttons. The buttons have the labels shown here:

Button	Label
Command1	Hex 278
Command2	Hex 378
Command3	Hex 3BC

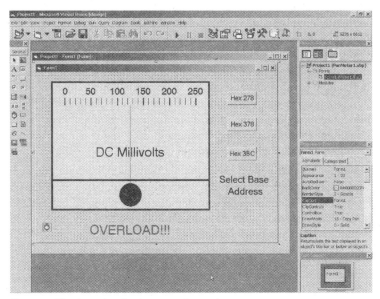

Fig7.41 The form for the improved panel meter program

One of the labels (Label4) simply gives an onscreen instruction to select the required base address. The other label (Label5) provides a red "OVERLOAD!!!" warning that is displayed on readings of more than 250. This is the full listing for the improved panel meter program:

```
Dim Prn1 As Integer
Dim Prn2 As Integer

Private Sub Command1_Click()
Prn1 = &H278
Prn2 = &H27A
Timer1.Enabled = True
Command1.Visible = False
Command2.Visible = False
Command3.Visible = False
Label4.Visible = False
End Sub
```

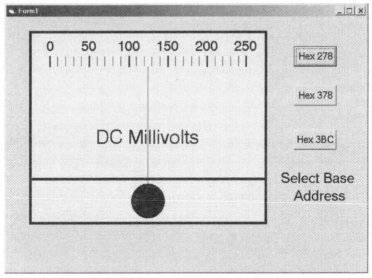

Fig.7.42 The initial appearance of the improved panel meter program

```
Private Sub Command2_Click()
Prn1 = &H378
Prn2 = &H37A
Timer1.Enabled = True
Command1.Visible = False
Command2.Visible = False
Command3.Visible = False
Label4.Visible = False
End Sub
Private Sub Command3_Click()
Prn1 = &H3BC
Prn2 = &H3BE
Timer1.Enabled = True
Command1.Visible = False
Command2.Visible = False
Command3.Visible = False
Label4.Visible = False
End Sub
```

```
Private Sub Timer1_Timer()
Out Prn2, 32
Raw = Inp(Prn1)
If Raw > 250 Then Label5.Visible = True
If Raw < 251 Then Label5.Visible = False
Raw = Raw * 20
Raw = Raw + 1100
Line1.X2 = Raw
End Sub
```

The first two lines declare global variables that will be used to hold the two port addresses used in the INP and OUT instructions used in the timer's subroutine. The subroutine for each command button is essentially the same. First the appropriate two addresses are assigned to variables Prn1 and Prn2. Then all three buttons and Label4 (the one containing the onscreen instruction) are switched off. The subroutine for Timer1 uses Prn1 and Prn2 to provide the port addresses in the INP and OUT instructions respectively.

Two additional lines set the Visible parameter of Label5 at True if the reading from the port is less than 251, or False if the reading is more than 250. In other words, the overload warning will be displayed for readings over 250, but will be suppressed for readings of 250 or less. Note that these two lines require the raw values from the port, and must therefore be placed before any of the mathematics performed on these values.

Figure 7.42 shows the program when it is initially run, complete with the three command buttons and the onscreen instruction. These disappear when a base address is selected by operating one of the buttons, and the meter then becomes active (Figure 7.43). The "OVERLOAD!!!" warning appears on readings of more than 250, as in Figure 7.44.

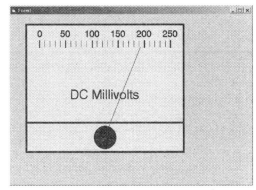

Fig.7.43 The improved program in operation

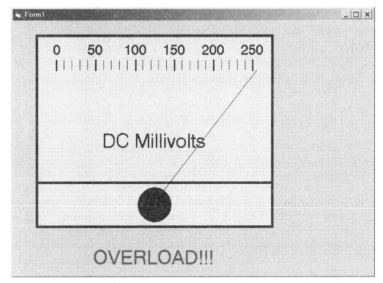

Fig.7.44 The meter program with the overload warning activated

Cheap VB

There are two or three options available if you would like to try out Visual BASIC without going to the expense of buying one of the normal retail editions. The best free version is the Visual BASIC 6.0 Working Model, which has been given away with a few computer magazines. Unfortunately, this version does not seem to be available as a download from the Microsoft web site, so unless you happen to have one of the free CD-ROMs that contain it, this version is not an option. If you can locate a copy, the Working Model edition does everything that the standard version can do, except that it is not possible to compile either an EXE file or a program group.

On the face of it, this renders the program useless. However, your programs can be run from within Visual BASIC, including the Working Model version. This means that you must have a version of Visual BASIC loaded before you can use your programs, but this is not a major hardship. The same is true of interpreted languages such as GW BASIC and QBASIC, and the Working Model version is effectively an interpreted version of Visual BASIC. Programs can be saved to disc, loaded again, modified, and so on. Using the Working Model you can therefore develop and store a range of software for use with your PC add-ons.

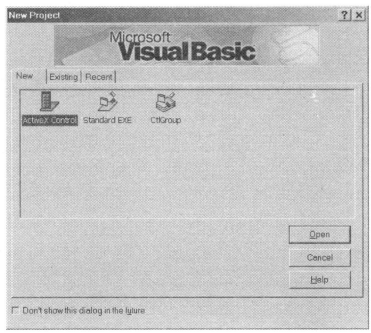

Fig.7.45 The Standard EXE option is available at the opening screen

VB5 CCE

If you can not obtain the Visual BASIC 6.0 Working model, the next best thing is Visual BASIC 5.0 Control Creation Edition. This is available as a download from the Microsoft web site, and the site's search engine should soon locate the program file and some documentation for it. As far as I can gather, version 6.0 of this edition has not been produced, but version 5.0 is perfectly adequate for producing software for PC add-ons. The intended purpose of this version is the production of ActiveX controls, but on running the program you get the opening screen of Figure 7.45. The number of options available is clearly far smaller than the number offered by the real thing, but the Control Creation Edition does have the all-important Standard EXE option.

Selecting this takes you into the main program, which looks very much like the equivalent in the normal versions of Visual BASIC 5.0 and 6.0 (Figure 7.46). There is the usual component palette on the left, the Properties window, etc., on the right, and the form plus concealed Code

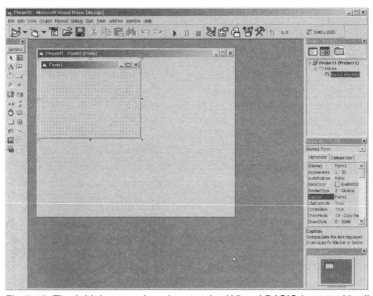

Fig.7.46 The initial screen has the standard Visual BASIC layout with all the normal elements present

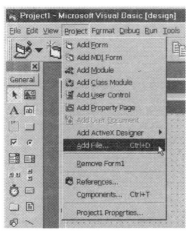

Fig.7.47 Inpout32.bas is added using the Add File option

window in the middle. The Project menu includes the Add file option (Figure 7.47) that can be used to load Inpout32.bas in the normal way. You then add components to the form, set their parameters using the Properties window, and add code into the Code window, just as you would using one of the retail versions of Visual BASIC.

When the program is finished it can be tested using the normal options under the Run menu. Figure 7.48 shows a simple port reading program in Visual BASIC 5.0 CCE, and Figure 7.49 shows this program in operation. This is all exactly the same as when using an ordinary edition of Visual

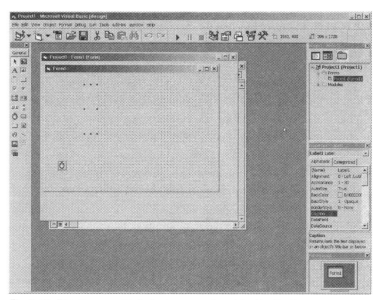

Fig.7.48 The timer and label components added to the form

BASIC 5.0 or 6.0. The normal Open and Save options are available under the File menu, but both Make options are greyed out and unavailable. Like the Visual BASIC 6.0 Working Model, this version can not be used to produce either an EXE file or a program group. Programs have to be run from within Visual

Fig.7.49 The port reading program running within Visual BASIC 5.0 CCE

BASIC 5.0 CCE itself, again giving what is effectively an interpreted version of Visual BASIC. However, with both the version 6.0 Working Model and the version 5.0 Control Creation Edition, programs should run at full speed provided the Run with Full Compile option is selected from the Run menu.

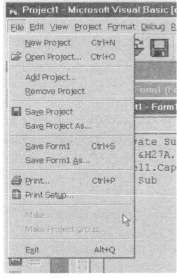

You are not limited to ultra simple programs, and the full range of components and instructions are available. Figure 7.51 shows a port writing program under construction in Visual BASIC 5.0 CCE, and this has command buttons, a label and horizontal scrollbar. Figure 7.52 shows the program in operation. The line and shape components are available, making it possible to produce pseudo analogue displays. In fact anything that can be undertaken using the standard editions of Visual BASIC 5.0 and 6.0 should be possible using this edition, apart from compiling programs of course.

Fig.7.50 The File menu options

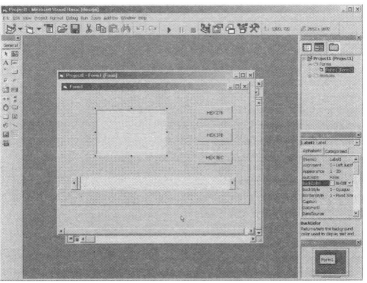

Fig.7.51 The usual components are all available, including scrollbars

Fig.7.52 The port writing program running within Visual BASIC 5.0 CCE

VBA

It is quite possible that your PC already has a form of Visual BASIC installed. Some of the more upmarket applications programs are supplied complete with Visual BASIC for Applications, or VBA as it is more commonly called. This is intended as a means of adding facilities to applications programs, and it is included with Microsoft Office and AutoCAD for example. The exact method of accessing VBA varies slightly

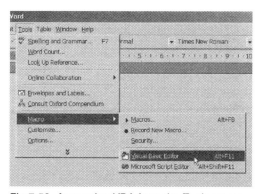

Fig.7.53 Accessing VBA from the Tools menu

from one program to another, but it is usually launched via the Tools menu of the main application. In Word for Windows 2000 for example, it

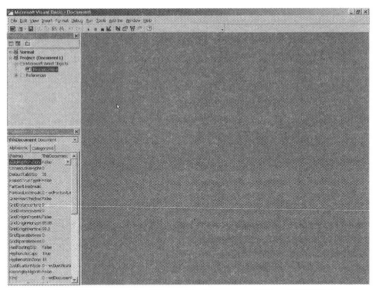

Fig.7.54 The VBA layout is different to the normal Visual BASIC type

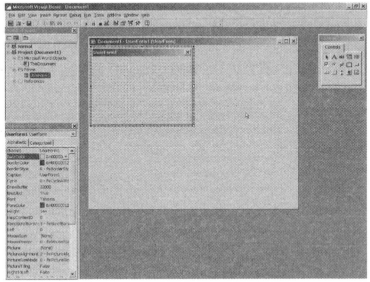

Fig.7.55 Things look more familiar with the form added

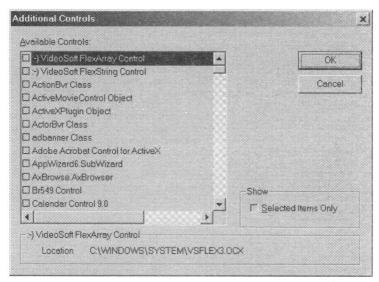

Fig.7.56 Additional components can be activated

is accessed via the Tools menu, and then the Macro submenu where the Visual Basic Editor option is selected (Figure 7.53).

Once into VBA it looks substantially different to the normal Visual BASIC environment (Figure 7.54). The obvious differences are the lack of the component palette, and the form is also absent. Both can be added to the main window by going to the Insert menu and selecting the User Form option. You then have the normal constituents of Visual BASIC, with the Properties window, form, etc., all present (Figure 7.55). However, the component palette is a cut-down version of the one found in Visual BASIC, and there are a few notable omissions, including the timer component.

More controls are available by selecting Additional Controls from the Tools menu. This produces a window like the one in Figure 7.56, where there is a checkbox for each of the available components. Tick the relevant checkbox to add a component to the palette, or remove a tick to clear the palette of an existing component. Unfortunately, most of the vast array of available controls are of no relevance to producing software for PC add-ons. It is still worth looking down the list in case you can find something of use. Incidentally, there is a similar facility available using

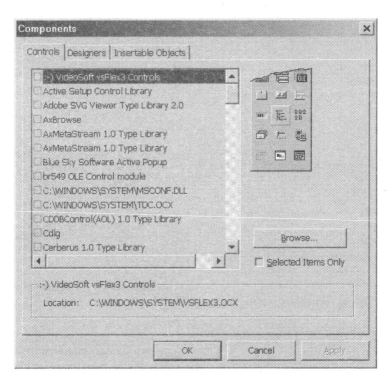

Fig.7.57 Additional tools are also available in Visual BASIC 6.0

Visual BASIC. Selecting Components from the Projects menu produces a window like the one shown in Figure 7.57.

Adding Inpout32.bas

In order to use with VBA with Inpout32.dll it is necessary to install Inpout32.bas first. This is achieved by selecting Import File from the File menu. The usual file browser appears and it is then just a matter of locating and selecting Inpout32.bas, and then operating the Open button. Inpout32 should then appear in the Project window (Figure 7.58), and the INP and OUT instructions should work correctly.

As an initial experiment with VBA, load Inpout32.bas and then add a scrollbar to the form. There is only one scrollbar component available using VBA, but it can act as a vertical or horizontal type. As Figure 7.59

shows, the type of scrollbar obtained depends on the aspect ratio of the rectangle dragged onto the form. Drag a tall and narrow rectangle to produce a vertical scrollbar, or a wide dumpy one if a horizontal scrollbar is required. For this example a horizontal scrollbar will be used, and its maximum value must be set at 255 using the Properties window. The default values should be satisfactory for the other parameters.

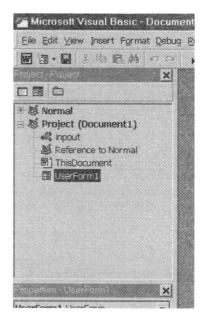

Fig.7.58 Inpout32 has been added

Next add a label component and adjust its parameters to give large digits, the required background colour, and so on. Double-click on the scrollbar to bring up the Code window and add these lines of code into the scrollbar's subroutine:

```
Label1.Caption = Scrollbar1.Value
Out &H378,Scrollbar1.Value
```

All this program does is to display the value read from the scrollbar on the label, and then output it to what will usually be printer port 1. Where appropriate, use a different port address in the second line. You should now have something like Figure 7.60, and the program should look

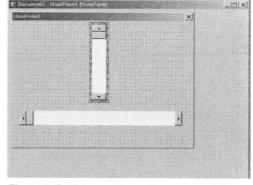

Fig.7.59 Both types of scrollbar are available

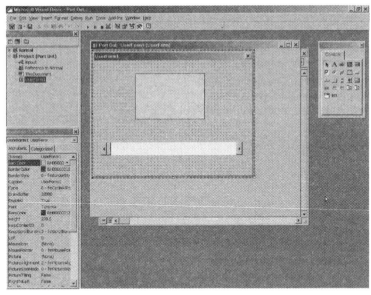

Fig.7.60 The simple port writing program being built in VBA

initially like Figure 7.61 when it is run. To run the program, select Run Sub/User Form from the Run menu. Operating the scrollbar should result in a value being output to the printer port and this value will also be shown on the digital display (Figure 7.62).

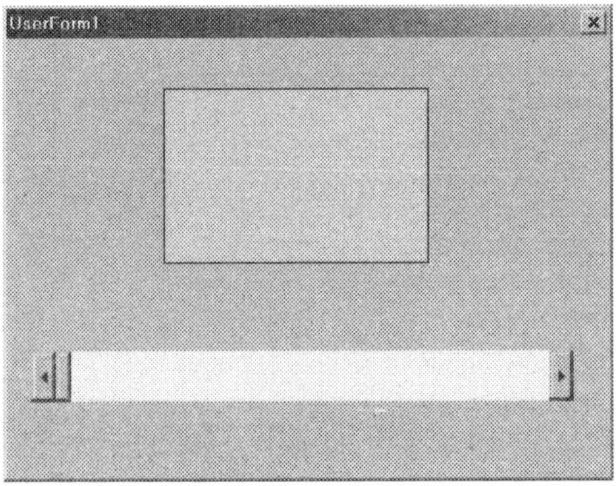

In order to save the program to disc, select Save from the File menu and save the current document as a normal Word DOC format file. To load the program again, go into Word for Windows, load the document that contains the program, and then

Fig.7.61 The initial appearance of the program

Fig.7.62 The program fully up and running in VBA

go to the Visual BASIC editor. Your program should already be loaded into the editor, complete with Inpout32.bas, and ready to run. Do not go into the Visual BASIC editor first and try to load the document from there. There is no way of doing this, and the document must be loaded into Word for Windows.

VBA is a relatively restrictive and clumsy way of producing Visual BASIC programs for your PC add-ons. It is still worth trying if you already have a suitable application program on your PC. You can make some initial experiments with Visual BASIC programming at no cost and the only download you will need is Inpout32. However, if you intend to do a lot of Visual BASIC programming it is better to either obtain Visual BASIC 5.0 CCE or one of the retail versions of Visual BASIC.

Other BASICs

Visual BASIC dominates the world of Windows programming, and you could be forgiven for thinking that it is the only BASIC programming language for Windows. This is not the case, and there are a few other BASIC programming languages for use under Windows. A search of

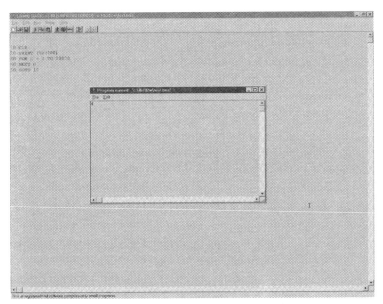

Fig.7.63 A simple program running within Liberty BASIC

the Internet should reveal some of the alternatives, such as a version of BBC BASIC for Windows, and Liberty BASIC. The latter is probably the most popular of the alternative BASIC languages, and a free demonstration version is available from www.libertybasic.com.

With a registered version of Liberty BASIC it is possible to use the supplied runtime module to produce programs that can run independently of Liberty BASIC. This feature is not available in the free demonstration program. Instead, the code is entered into the main window, and a separate program window appears when the program is run from within Liberty BASIC. In other words, it operates more or less as a traditional interpreted BASIC. Figure 7.63 shows a very simple program running, and this repeatedly reads printer port 1 and prints the returned value in the program window. This is the program I used:

```
10 CLS
20 PRINT INP(888)
30 FOR D = 1 TO 20000
40 NEXT D
50 GOTO 10
```

The line numbers are optional, and labels can be used for unconditional branches. As this program demonstrates, Liberty BASIC is much more like a conventional BASIC language than Visual BASIC, and it should appeal to those who require an MS-DOS style BASIC that produces Windows programs. Both INP and OUT instructions are included as a standard part of Liberty BASIC, so there is no need for any ActiveX controls or DLL files.

Windows XP

As pointed out previously, Windows NT4, 2000, and XP can not be used with Inpout32.dll, or with a BASIC programming language that has the INP and OUT instructions built-in. Neither can they be used with programs that use assembly language routines to access the input/output ports.

These operating systems do not permit programs to directly access the ports, but instead insist on programs using the ports via the operating system. With the operating system controlling access to the ports there is no danger of two programs trying to simultaneously access the same port. This aids good stability and makes Windows NT4, 2000, and XP less prone to crashing than Windows 95, 98, and ME. It inevitably complicates the process of writing software for PC based electronic projects though.

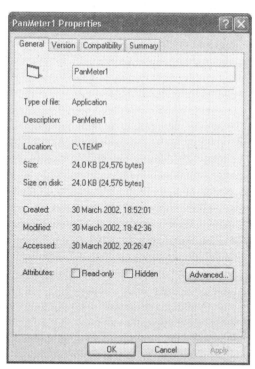

Fig.7.64 The Properties window for a program

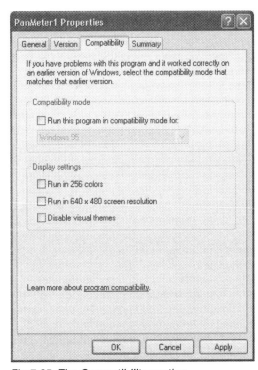

Fig.7.65 The Compatibility section

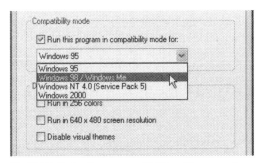

Fig.7.66 Selecting compatibility with an earlier version of Windows

It is sometimes suggested that Windows XP can be made to operate with programs that break its input/output rules by using its compatibility feature. This feature permits programs to be run in a so-called compatibility mode. If a program worked previously with (say) Windows 95, but it fails to work when used under Windows XP, then, then setting the compatibility mode to Windows 95 should get the program working under Windows XP. Setting a compatibility mode is easy enough, but it is only fair to point out that this method is unlikely to work with programs that directly access the ports.

In order to use a compatibility mode, first find the appropriate program file using Windows Explorer. Program files are executable files that have an "exe" extension.

Having located the correct file, right-click on it to produce a popup menu, and then select Properties from that menu. A properties window like the one in Figure 7.64 will then appear, showing some general information about the program file. Operating the Compatibility tab changes the window to one like Figure 7.65, and here the Compatibility Mode checkbox should be ticked. The menu immediately beneath it then becomes active and the required level of compatibility can be selected (Figure 7.66).

Disabling ports

Another ploy is to disable the port you are trying to access if it is one of the standard ports such as a printer or serial type. This effectively persuades Windows XP to loosen its grip on the port, which it will otherwise tend to guard against any external interference. This method can also be used with other versions of Windows if your program and the operating system both try to control a port. To disable a port, start by selecting Control Panel from the Start menu, and then double click on the System icon or text entry. This launches the System Properties window (Figure 7.67) where the Hardware tab is operated, followed by the Device Manager button when the new version of the window appears.

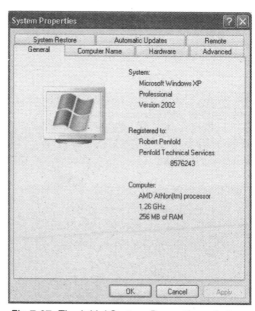

Fig.7.67 The initial System Properties window

Next, double-click on the Ports (Com and Lpt) entry to expand it, and then right-click on the entry for the appropriate port. This will produce a popup menu (Figure 7.69) where the Disable option is selected. Operate

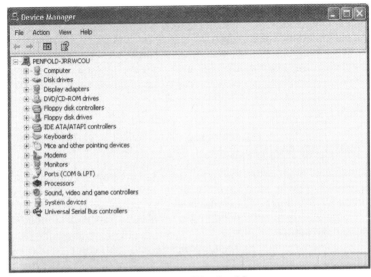

Fig.7.68 The Windows XP version of Device Manager

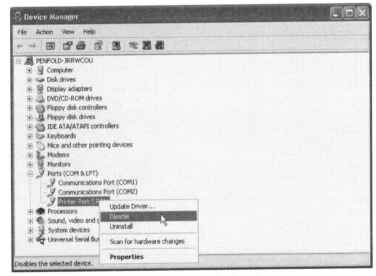

Fig.7.69 Selecting and disabling a standard port

the Yes button when you are asked to confirm that you wish to disable this port. A red cross will then appear across the entry for the port to indicate that it has been successfully deactivated (Figure 7.70).

Fig.7.70 The red cross shows that the port is disabled

In practice Windows XP is not easily persuaded to give access to the ports, and all this is unlikely to help. Figure 7.71 shows the panel meter project running under Windows XP using Windows 95 compatibility and the printer port disabled. It looks quite plausible, but it should be displaying a reading of 255 with overload warning in operation. It is not causing any instability in Windows XP, but it is not working properly either. These two ploys might be more effective with other methods of accessing the ports, but they do not seem to work with Windows XP and Inpout32.dll.

There are add-ons specifically for providing port access under Windows NT4, 2000, and XP. Some built-in port handling facilities go through the

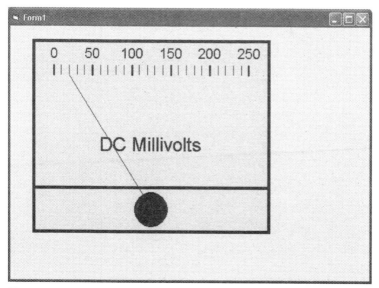

Fig.7.71 The panel meter program running under Windows XP

official channels and should work properly with these operating systems. A utility worth investigating is the Tinyport program, which is available via the www.lvr.com site mentioned previously. It is only fair to point out that port access utilities for use with Windows NT4, etc., are generally much less straightforward in use than Inpout32.dll. Also, some of them require programs to be run in a compatibility mode under Windows XP, and may additionally require standard ports to be disabled using Device Manager. Where possible it is better to use Windows 95, 98, or ME, where direct port accesses are permitted, and these complications are avoided.

Points to remember

Programs produced using visual programming languages are event driven. The relevant subroutine is executed when an event occurs, such as the user operating a button or selecting a menu item. Conventional program structures are not relevant to programs produced using a visual programming language.

Delphi 1 has a Port command that provides access to the input and output ports. Unfortunately, this facility is not included in the later versions of Delphi, although the in-line assembler provides a reasonably straightforward means of accessing ports.

No version of Visual BASIC has INP and OUT instructions, or any equivalent to them. However, these instructions or something similar can be added using an ActiveX control or a dynamic link library (DLL) file. Inpout32 is probably the easiest add-on that provides this facility, and it is free.

Using a visual programming language such as Visual BASIC it is easy to produce neat user interfaces that have control buttons, digital readouts, menus, etc. The basic screen layout can be produced without resorting to any programming, and changes are easily made.

You still need some programming skills in order to use a Visual programming language. Having produced the screen layout, none of the buttons, labels, menus, etc., will do anything until you write the code that makes them work. Fortunately, you do not have to be an expert programmer in order to produce the software for most PC add-ons.

Using the basic drawing tools of Visual BASIC it is easy to produce pseudo analogue displays such as bargraphs and panel meters. These are preferable to digital readouts in certain applications. In particular, they are better where readings will be changing quite rapidly, which tends to give confusing results using a digital readout.

There are at least a few alternatives to Visual BASIC if you require a BASIC programming language for use with Windows. These are mostly traditional BASIC languages that should appeal to those who do not like the visual approach to programming.

Direct port access is not permitted with Windows XP, or with the Windows NT4 and Windows 2000 operating systems. There are ploys that can be used in an attempt to make Windows XP work with programs that access the ports. However, programs are unlikely to work with this operating system, or with Windows NT4 and 2000, unless ports are accessed via the operating system.

Programs should work with Windows XP if they use built-in facilities of the programming language that do things via the approved channels. Alternatively, there are various types of add-on available that permit the ports to be accessed when using Windows NT4, 2000, and XP. Unfortunately, these add-ons tend to be far less straightforward in use than Inpout32.

Index

Index